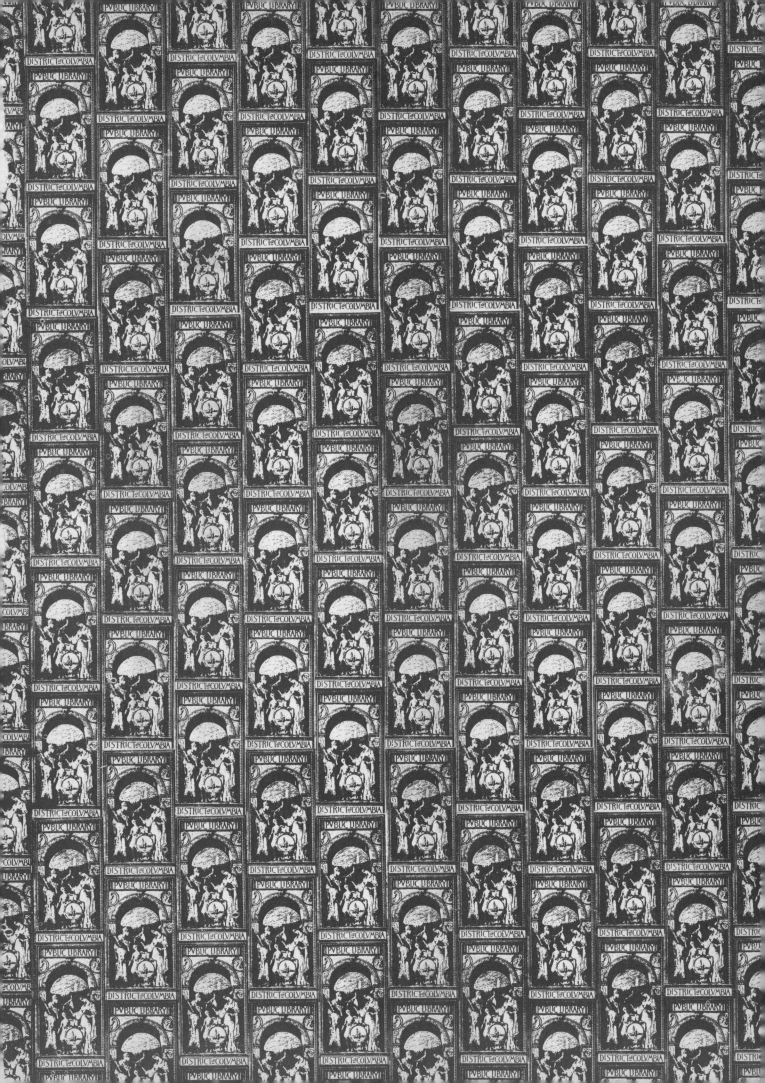

**MAMMOTH SERIES No. 17**

*Robbins*

# MAMMOTH

## COLLECTION OF

## SONGS OF THE GAY NINETIES

Edited and Arranged by
### HUGO FREY

Copyright 1942
## ROBBINS MUSIC CORPORATION
799 SEVENTH AVENUE · NEW YORK

# CONTENTS

# I Wish I Had A Girl

Lyric by
GUS KAHN

Melody by
GRACE LE BOY

# Hello! Ma Baby

JOSEPH E. HOWARD
IDA EMERSON

# On A Saturday Night

JOS. E. HOWARD

Arr. by Hugo Frey

# Roll On, Silver Moon

J. W. TURNER

Moderately slow

As I stray'd from my cot __ at the close of the day, 'Mid the
As the hart on the moun - tain, my lov - er was brave, So no-

rav - ish-ing beau-ties of June, ___ 'Neath a jes - sa - mine shade, I es-
ble and man-ly and clev - er, ___ So kind and sin - cere, And he

pied a fair maid, __ And she plain - tive - ly sighed to the moon. ___
loved me full dear, __ Oh, my Ed-win, his e - qual was nev - er! ___

Chorus

Roll __ on, sil-ver moon, Guide the trav-'ler his way, While the night-in-gale's song is in tune; __ I __

nev-er, nev-er more with my true love will stray __ by thy soft __ sil-ver beams, Gen-tle moon. ___

*Arr. by Hugo Frey*

# A Rose With A Broken Stem

Words by
CARROLL FLEMING

Music by
EVERETT J. EVANS

1. At a gay mas - que - rade in a ball room grand, two
2. When the mask fell a - way from the gip - sy's brow, they

beau - ti - ful maids were there,_____ And
knew what the Rose had done,_____ For

Leo Feist, Inc., 1629 Broadway, New York, N. Y.

one bore a rose in her jewelled hand, the oth-er a lil-y
she had been false to the sa-cred vow, she gave to the gip-sy's

fair,———— "The Rose shall be queen" then the dan-cers said, the
son,———— Her heart she had sold for a mis-ers gold, a

Lil-y turned a-way,———— But the beau-ti-ful Rose sad-ly
mi-ser old and gray,———— And the bells that had rung for her

bowed her head, as she heard an old gip-sy say:————
wed-ding tolled, for the lad that had passed a-way.————

Chorus (*Valse lento*)

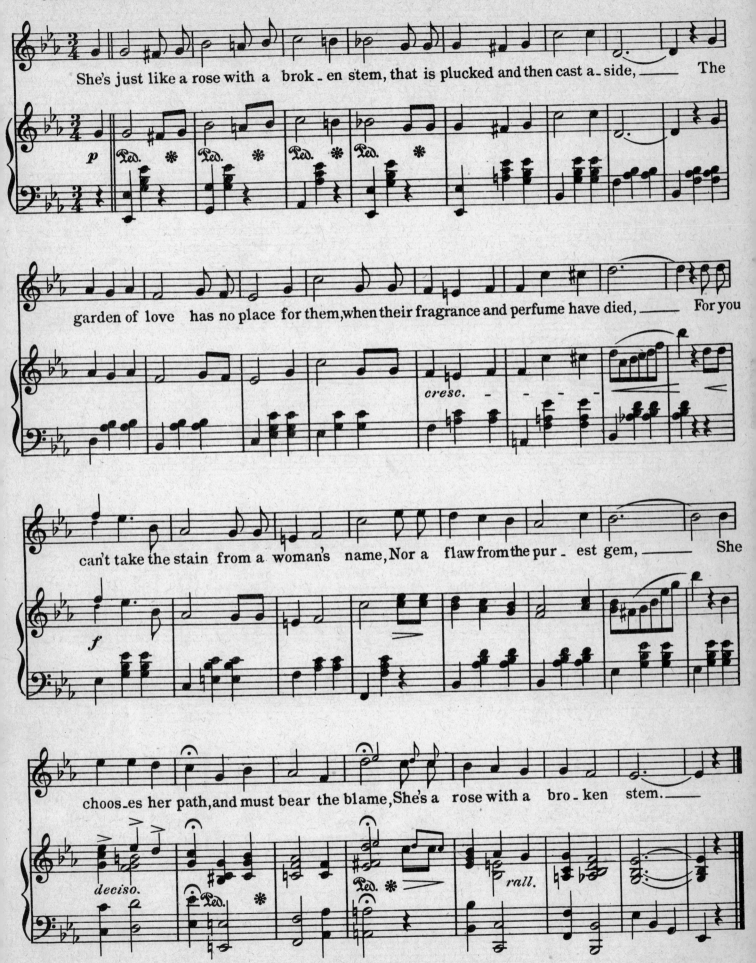

She's just like a rose with a brok _ en stem, that is plucked and then cast a _ side, _____ The

garden of love has no place for them, when their fragrance and perfume have died, _____ For you

can't take the stain from a woman's name, Nor a flaw from the pur _ est gem, _____ She

choos _ es her path, and must bear the blame, She's a rose with a bro _ ken stem. _____

# Breakfast In My Bed On Sunday Mornin'

GERALD GRAFTON
HARRY LAUDER

Arr. by Hugo Frey

Chorus, Moderato

To beau - ti - ful Sun - day! I wish it would nev-er come Mon-day! For I
(On beau - ti - ful) Sun - day! I wish it would nev-er come Mon-day! For I

lie be-tween the sheets my bed_ a - dorn - in'. O, it's ver-y nice! yes, it's
lie be-tween the sheets my bed_ a - dorn - in'. O, it's ver-y nice! yes, it's

ver - y, ver - y nice To get yer break-fast in yer bed on Sun - day
ver - y, ver - y nice To get yer break-fast in yer bed on Sun - day

1.
morn - in'! On beau - ti - ful

2.
morn - in'!

# Can't You See I'm Lonely

By
FELIX F. FEIST
HENRY ARMSTRONG
*New Version by Gus Kahn
and Carmen Lombardo*

# Down Among The Sheltering Palms

Lyric by
JAMES BROCKMAN

Music by
ABE OLMAN

*New Arr. by Lee Orean Smith*

Just you, I know,___ It takes six days to go there with a train, Just
None could com - pare,___ There's on - ly one place 'way out in the West, And

one week more, and I'll be with you a - gain.___ I long to be
you are there, where with you I long to rest.___ I long to be

**CHORUS**
*(a little faster)*

Down_____ a - mong the shel - ter - ing palms, O hon - ey, wait for me,

___ O hon - ey, wait for me;___ Meet me___ down by the

old Gold-en Gate, ___ Out where ___ the sun goes down a-bout eight. ___

How my love ___ is burn-ing, burn-ing, burn-ing, How my heart ___ is

yearn-ing, yearn-ing, yearn-ing to be Down ___ a-mong the shel-ter-ing palms, O hon-ey,

**1.**  **2**

wait for me! ___ me! ___ *D.S.*

# Dear Old Girl

Words by
RICHARD HENRY BUCK

Music by
THEODORE MORSE

Andante moderato

# M-O-T-H-E-R
## (A Word That Means The World To Me)

Lyric by
HOWARD JOHNSON

Music by
THEODORE MORSE

# A Picture No Artist Can Paint

J. FRED HELF

Arr. by LEE OREAN SMITH

# Somebody's Waiting For Me

Words by
ANDREW STERLING

Music by
HARRY VON TILZER

burst of laugh-ter rang out, as he stood there, hat in hand, Why it's
led them to a cot-tage, point-ed through the win-dow pane, Where a

on - ly twelve o'-clock, then some one cried.____ And an-y
gray-haired wo - man sat, with bowed-down head.____ "It's my

oth - er said sit down Jack, why the fun has just com-menced, But he
moth - er, she's my sweetheart, it was her I meant to-night, So you

slow - ly shook his head as he re - plied:____
see I told the truth, boys, when I said:____

31

Chorus (*Slowly*)

Some-bod-y's wait-ing for me, ___ Some-one who loves me I know, ___

Some-bod-y's won-der-ing where I can be, and what can be keep-ing me so; ___

Some-bod-y's heart is sad, ___ Watch-ing so anx-ious-ly, ___ There's a

light shining bright, In the window to-night For there's some-bod-y wait-ing for me. ___

# Just Plain Folks

By
MAURICE STONEHILL

# The Cat Came Back

Words and Music by
HARRY S. MILLER

*New Arr. by Theodore Morse*

CHORUS

But the cat came back, could-n't stay no long-er Yes, the cat came back, the ver-y next day, The cat came back, thought he was a gon-er, But the cat came back for it would-n't stay a-way.

3. On a telegraph wire sparrows sitting in a bunch,
   Cat a feeling hungry, thought she'd like 'em for a lunch,
   Climbing softly up de pole, an' when she reached de top,
   Put her foot upon de 'lectric wire, which tied her in a knot.

4. One time did gib de cat away to man in a balloon,
   An' tole him for to gib it to de man in de moon;
   But de b'loon it busted, sho, an' eb'rybody sed
   It wer seben miles away or more dey picked de man up dead.

5. De cat was a possessor ob a fam'ly ob its own,
   Wid seben little kittens till dar comes a cyclone,
   Blowed de houses all apart and tossed de cat around;
   While de air was full ob kittens not a one was eber found.

6. De cat it were a terror and dey said it wer be best
   To gib it to a darkey who was going out West,
   De train going 'round de curve struck a broken rail,
   Not a blessed soul aboad de train was left to tell de tale.

7. A man down on de corner swore to kill de cat at sight,
   Loaded up a musket full ob nails and dynamite,
   Waited in de garden for de cat to come around,
   Half a-dozen little pieces ob de man was all dey found.

8. While de cat lay a sleeping an' a resting one day,
   'Round came an organ grinder an he began to play;
   De cat look'd around awhile an' kinder raised her head
   When he played Ta-rah-rah-boom-de-ay, an' de cat dropped dead!

# A Bicycle Built For Two
## (Daisy Bell)

Arranged by Hugo Frey

Words and Music by
**HARRY DACRE**

*Waltz tempo*

There is a flow-er with-in my heart, Dai - sy,
We will go "Tan-dem" as man and wife, Dai - sy,
I will stand by you in "wheel" or woe, Dai - sy,

Dai - sy! Plant-ed one day by a glanc - ing dart,
Dai - sy! "Ped'- ling" a - way down the road of life,
Dai - sy! You'll be the bell(e) which I'll ring, you know!

Planted by Daisy Bell!_____ Whether she loves me or loves me
I and my Daisy Bell!_____ When the road's dark we can both de-
Sweet little Daisy Bell!_____ You'll take the "lead" in each "trip"

not, Some-times it's hard to tell;_____ Yet I am
spise P'lice-men and "lamps" as well;_____ There are"bright
take, Then, if I don't do well;_____ I will per-

long-ing to share the lot of beau-ti-ful Dai - sy Bell!_____
lights"in the dazz-ling eyes of beau-ti-ful Dai - sy Bell!_____
mit you to use the brake, my beau-ti-ful Dai - sy Bell!_____

rit.

**Chorus** (*with marked rhythm*)

Dai - sy, Dai - sy, Give me your an - swer, do,_____

mf

# While Strolling Thru The Park One Day

### In The Merry Month Of May

by
ED HALEY

Transcription by
Hugo Frey

Ah! I im - me - di - ate - ly rais'd my
hat, And fi - nal - ly she re - mark'd: I
nev - er shall for - get, that love - ly af - ter - noon, I
met her at the foun - tain in the park.

# The Band Played On

Words by
JOHN F. PALMER

CHARLES B. WARD

44

# The Bowery

Words by
CHARLES H. HOYT

Music by
PERCY GAUNT

Copyright 1942 **ROBBINS MUSIC CORPORATION**, 799 Seventh Ave., New York, N. Y.

# Dreaming

Poem by
L.W. HEISER

Music by
J. ANTON DAILEY

Moderately slow (*with expression*)

Out in the still sum-mers eve - ning In - to my heart comes a feel - ing
Years have gone by, still I love you Tho' there's an - oth - er who won you

of love that's true and un - dy - ing; For you, sweet-heart, I am sigh - ing.
out of my life you have drift - ed; Yet in my heart You still lin - ger.

Down by the stream, where we wan - der'd Un - der the pale moon-light beam - ing,
Dream-ing or wak - ing I see you, I can for-give, not for - get you

There's where I lin - ger and dream of you Dar - ling Dream - ing.——
In life and death I'll a - wait your re - turn while I'm Dream - ing.——

Arr. by Hugo Frey

# Father, Dear Father Come Home With Me Now!

HENRY C. WORK

Arr. by Hugo Frey

poor broth-er Ben - ny so sick in her arms, With - out you, oh, what can she do?___ Come
this is the mes-sage she sent me to bring, "Come quick - ly, or he will be gone."___ Come
these were the ver - y last words that he said, "I want to kiss Pa - pa good - night."___ Come

home! Come home! Come home!___ Please, fa-ther, dear_ fa - ther, come home.___
home! Come home! Come home!___ Please, fa-ther, dear_ fa - ther, come home.___
home! Come home! Come home!___ Please, fa-ther, dear_ fa - ther, come home.___

Chorus, Moderately slow

Hear the sweet voice of your own lit-tle child, As she tear-ful-ly begs you to come!___ Oh,

who could re-sist this most pit-i-ful pray'r, "Please, fa-ther, dear fa-ther, come home!"___

# Hello Central, Give Me Heaven

Words and Music by
CHAS. K. HARRIS

Slowly (with expression)

Pa - pa I'm so sad and lone-ly, / Sobbed a tear-ful lit-tle
When the girl re-ceived this mes-sage, / Com - ing o'er the tel - e-

child, ___ / Since dear ma-ma's gone to heav - en,
phone, ___ / How her heart thrilled in that mo - ment,

Pa - pa dar-ling you've not smiled, ___ / I will speak to her and
And the wi - res seemed to moan, ___ / I will an - swer just to

tell her, / That we want her to come home,
please her, / Yes dear heart, I'll soon come home,

Arr. by Hugo Frey

Just you lis-ten and I'll call her, Through the tel - e - phone.___
Kiss me ma-ma, kiss your dar - ling, Through the tel - e - phone.___

**Chorus, Slowly** (*with expression*)

Hel - lo Cen - tral, give me heav - en, For my ma - ma's there,___

You can find her with the an - gels on the gold - en stair,___

She'll be glad it's me who's speak - ing, call her won't you please,

For I want to sure - ly tell her, We're so lone - ly here.___

# I Guess I'll Have To Telegraph My Baby

Words and Music by
GEORGE M. COHAN

Arr. by Hugo Frey

Will-iams and_ Walk-er Would soon have to take off their hats and sa-
self, he was a-talk-in', Said he, "No more troup-in' or trav-'lin' is

laam! In a town they land-ed, troupe dis-band-ed, they were strand-ed,
mine." Be- fore the judge, he had to trudge, he did-n't budge; the

emp-ty hand-ed; Then an ac-tor said to him,"What will you do now,
land-lord's grudge Brought sen-tence of two years in jail, or twen-ty dol-lars

Sam?" He sighed and cried, and then he re- plied:
fine. He sighed and cried, and then he re- plied:

Chorus, Lively

"Well, I guess I'll have to tel-e-graph my ba - by, I need the mon-ey

bad, in-deed I do;_____ For Lu-cy is a ver-y gen'rous la-

dy, I can al-ways touch her for a few._____ I find the West-ern

Un-ion a — con - ven - ience, No mat-ter where I roam.

_ I'll tel - e-graph my ba - by, she'll send ten or twen-ty, may-be; Then I

1.
won't have to walk back home." "Well, I

2.
home."_____

# Throw Him Down Mc Closkey

Words and Music by
J. W. KELLY

'Twas down at Dan Mc De-vitt's at the cor-ner of this street, There
The fight-ers were to start in at a quar-ter af-ter eight, The
They fought like two hy-e-nas till the for-ty-sev-enth round, They

was to be a prize fight and both par-ties were to meet; To make all the ar-
dark-y did not show up and the hour was get-ting late; He sent a-round a
scat-tered blood e-nough a-round by gosh to paint the town, Mc Clos-key got a

range-ments and see ev-'ry-thing was right Mc Clos-key and a dark-y were to
mes-sen-ger who then went on to say, That the I-rish crowd would jump him and he
mouth-ful of poor Mc Crack-ens jowl. Mc Crack-en hol-lered "mur-ther" and his

*Arr. by Hugo Frey*

Copyright 1942 **ROBBINS MUSIC CORPORATION**, 799 Seventh Ave., New York, N.Y.

have a fin - ish fight; The rules were Lon-don prize ring and Mc Clos-key said he'd
could-n't get fair play; Then up steps Pete Mc Crack-en, and said that he would
sec-onds hol-lered "foul"! The friends of both the fight-ers that in-stant did be-

try, To bate the dark - y with one punch or in the ring he'd die, The
fight. Stand up, or rough and tum-ble, if Mc Clos-key did-n't bite, Mc
gin To fight and ate each oth - er the whole par-ty start-ed in, You

odds were on Mc Clos-key though the bet-ting it was small, 'Twas
Clos-key says I'll go you, then the sec-onds got in place, And the
could-n't tell the dif-f'rence 'mong the fight-ers if you'd try, Mc

on Mc Clos-key ten to one on the dark-y none at all. ____
fight-ers start-ed in to dec-o - rate each oth-ers face. ____
Crack-en lost an up-per lip, Mc Clos-key lost an eye. ____

Chorus, Brightly

Throw him down Mc Clos-key, was to be the bat-tle cry,____

Throw him down Mc Clos-key, You can lick him if you try; And

fu-ture gen-er-a-tions, With won-der and de-light, Will____

read on his-t'rys pag-es of the great Mc Clos-key fight.

D.S.

D.S.

# Who Threw The Overalls
# In Mistress Murphy's Chowder

Words and Music
GEO. L. GEIFER

*Arr. by Hugo Frey*

# My Gal Is A High Born Lady

Words and Music by
BARNEY FAGAN

Moderately (Cake Walk)

Thar' is gwine to be a fes-ti-val this eve-nin', And a
When the preach-er man pro-pounds the vi-tal ques-tion "Does ye'

gath-er-in' of col-or might-y rare, ___ Thar'll be not-ed in-di-vid-u-als of
take the gal for bet-ter or for wuss?" ___ I will feel as if my soul had left my

prom-i-nent dis-tinc-tive-ness, To per-me-ate the col-or'd at-mos-
bod-y, gone to glo-ry, And I know my heart will make an aw-ful

phere. ___ Sun-ny Af-ri-ca's Four Hun-dred's gwine to be thar, To do
fuss. ___ I an-ti-ci-pates a ver-y fun-ny feel-in' Dark-ie's

hon-or to my love-ly fi-an-cee, ___ Thar' will be a grand o-va-tion of es-
eye-fall, like a dia-mond sure to shine ___ But I'll bask in hon-eyed clo-ver, when the

*Arr. by Hugo Frey*

Copyright 1942 **ROBBINS MUSIC CORPORATION**, 799 Seventh Ave., New York, N. Y.

spec-ial os-ten-ta-tion, When the par-son gives the dusk-y bride a-way.___
cer-e-mon-y's o-ver, And I press the ru-by lips of ba-by mine.___

**Chorus, Slower**

My gal is a high born la-dy, She's dark but none too shad-y,

Feath-er'd like a pea-cock, just as gay, She is not col-or'd, she was

born that way.___ I'm proud of my dark Ven-us, No man can come be-tween us,

'Long the line they can't out-shine This high born gal of mine.    mine.___

# Ain't Dat A Shame

Words by
JOHN QUEEN

Music by
WALTER WILSON

Arr. by Hugo Frey

to the house he went, Oh lis-ten to _____ his mourn-ful cry. _____

roost here an-y-more,"And pass-ers by _____ could hear Bill cry. _____

**Chorus, Moderately**

Ain't dat a shame, _____ a meas-ly shame, _____ To keep your

hon-ey _____ out in the rain, (Lordy have a little pity) _____ Will you o-pen dat

door, _____ and let me in, _____ I stand yere freez-in'

1.
— wet to the skin. _____ Ain't dat a

2.
skin. _____

# Down Went McGinty

JOSEPH FLYNN

Sun - day morn-ing just at nine, Dan Mc - Gin - ty dress'd so fine, Stood look-
From the hospi-tal Mac went home, When they fix'd his bro - ken bones, To find
Now Mc - Gin - ty raved and swore, 'Bout his clothes he felt so sore, And an
Now Mc - Gin - ty thin and pale, One fine day got out of jail, And with

ing up at a ver - y high stone wall; When his friend young Pat Mc-Cann, Says, "I'll
he was the — fa-ther of a child; So to cel - e - brate it right, his friends
oath he took he'd kill the man or die; So he tight - ly grabb'd his stick and hit
joy to see his boy was near-ly wild; To his house he quick - ly ran To meet

bet five dol - lars, Dan, I could car-ry you to the top with-out — a
he went to in - vite, And he soon was drink-ing whis-ky fast and
the driv - er a lick, Then he raised a lit - tle shan-ty on his
his wife Be - daley Ann, But she'd skipp'd a - way and took a - long the

Chorus, Allegro moderato

# Has Your Mother Any More Like You

## By ROBERT A. KEISER

70

# Aura Lee

*Transcription by*
**HUGO FREY**

# Does True Love Ever Run Smooth?

LEO FEIST

Waltz (*Moderately*)

Lau - ra and May, lov - ing sis - ters were they, And con - stant com -
"Cheer up," said May, "he'll re - turn home some day, I'm sure that he

pan - ions as well; _____ Soon May was to mar - ry
loves none but you; _____ So dry those sad tears, love;

her sweet - heart Har - ry, And she was glad, one could tell. _____
cast off your fears, love; You'll find his heart staunch and true." _____

*Arr. by Hugo Frey*

One day, Lau - ra said, "Sis - ter, soon you'll be wed, And
Such words, good and kind, soon eased Lau - ra's mind, Just

then, oh! how lone-some I'll be; For Jack's gone a year, and
then the door o - pened wide, She sprang to her feet and

some-times I fear He nev - er will come back to me."
has - tened to greet The sweet-heart for whom she had cried.

Chorus, Waltz (Moderately)

Oh! how I love him, if he but

knew! _____ How I have missed him and longed

for him too! _____ Why don't he write, my

an - guish to soothe? _____ Tell me does true

love ev - er run smooth? smooth? _____

# The Letter Edged In Black

Words and Music by
HATTIE NEVADA

Edited by D. SAVINO

Andante

I was stand-ing by my win-dow yes-ter morn-ing, With-
Then, with trem-bling hands, I took the let-ter from him, I
Oh, I bow my head in sad-ness and in sor-row, The

out a thought of wor-ry or of care,___ When I saw the Post-man com-ing down the
broke the seal, and this is what it said:___ "Come___ home my boy, your poor old Fa-ther
sun-light of my life it now has fled,___ Since the Post-man brought that let-ter yes-ter

path-way, With such a hap-py smile and jaun-ty air.___ Oh he
wants you, Come home my boy, your Moth-er dear is dead."___ Oh your
morn-ing, Say-ing;"Come my boy, your Moth-er dear is dead."___ Oh it

Refrain

As I heard the Post-man whist-ling yes-ter-morn-ing,

Com-ing down the path-way with his pack; Oh, he

lit-tle knew the sor-row that he brought me When he

hand-ed me a Let-ter Edged In Black.

# My Sweetheart's The Man In The Moon

JAMES THORNTON

Ev-'ry-bod - y has a sweet-heart un-der-neath the rose, Ev-'ry-bod-y loves a bod-y so the old song goes, I've a sweet-heart, you all know him just as well as me, Ev-'ry eve-ning I can see him short-ly af-ter tea.

Copyright 1942 ROBBINS MUSIC CORPORATION, 799 Seventh Ave., New York, N.Y.

# Scanlan's Rose Song

W. J. Scanlan

Arr. by HUGO FREY

# Aren't You The Girl I Met At Sherry's

Words by
FELIX F. FEIST

Music by
JOEL P. CORI[N]

Moderato.

*ff*

Vamp.

*p*

*mp*

I have trav-elled man-y miles, I've re-
I am not a keen ob-ser-ver, And per-

ceived some pleas-ant smiles, With the gen-tle sex I've al-ways been a
haps I don't de-serve her, But I don't pro-pose to let that in-ter-

pet;_____ I've been luck-y you might say, But the
fere;_____ I'm de-ter-mined I shall win her, She was

girl to get a-way, Like the North-ern Pole is un-dis-cov-ered
such a lit-tle sin-ner, That I'll nev-er rest un-til I have her

yet.___ The oth-er night while din-ing I could pict-ure Tri-ni-ty, My
here.___ That she's a-round is cer-tain, and she'll nev-er get a-way, I

eyes were met by what I thought, was my af-fin-i-ty; She
don't care what the cost may be, the bills I'll glad-ly pay; The

smiled at me so rog-uish-ly, my brain be-gan to whirl, I'm
search may be a length-y one, but that cuts lit-tle ice, She

on her track, I want her back, say, "are - n't you the girl?
must be mine, that maid di - vine, at an - y sac - ri - fice.

*rall.*

**Chorus.** *p f*

Are - n't you the girl I met at Sher-ry's? Are - n't you the maid that smiled at

*p-f*

me?_____ Were - n't you in - dulg - ing in black-

ber - ries? Were - n't you a sip-ping at some tea? I'm

al - most sure you are the ver - y la - dy,

Though per - haps there may be room for doubt;

Are - n't you the girl I met at Sher - ry's?

Just be - fore the lights went out. out.

# It Ain't All Honey And It Ain't All Jam

by
FRED MURRAY
GEO. EVERARD

Words and Music

1. With my love - ly hus - band to -
2. Fan - cy, twen - ty hours, and I
3. When I wed my hus - band, I

day I land-ed here, By a cheap ex-cur-sion train be - cause it wasn't dear,
hav-n't had a drink, I feel in-clined to push the Pram - bu - la - tor down a sink,
thought it jol - ly fine, Told me all my life that I should have the best of wine,"

Left me at the sta-tion, told me not to fret, While he went to look for rooms, he's
But I think the best thing for ba-by, pret-ty lamb, Is shove it on the par-ish, then I
But on me, for champagne he's never spent a "quid," The on-ly wine that I get is the

look-ing for 'em yet. That's ex-act-ly twen-ty hours a-go; I
think I'll pawn the "Pram." He's done this thing ma-ny ma-ny times,
"whin-ing" of the "kid." It ain't fair, no fare for the train have I, I'll

thought some-how he was-n't com-ing back, But when I do lay hold of him there's
Run a-way and left me, what a life! I'll bet while I'm a walking round a-
have to walk, I have-n't got a "cent," I'm fif-ty mile a-way from home, but

going to be some fun, I on-ly want to get up-on his track.
look-ing af-ter him, He's look-ing af-ter some-one-else's wife.
when I do get there, I'll take a lodg-er in to pay the rent.

CHORUS.

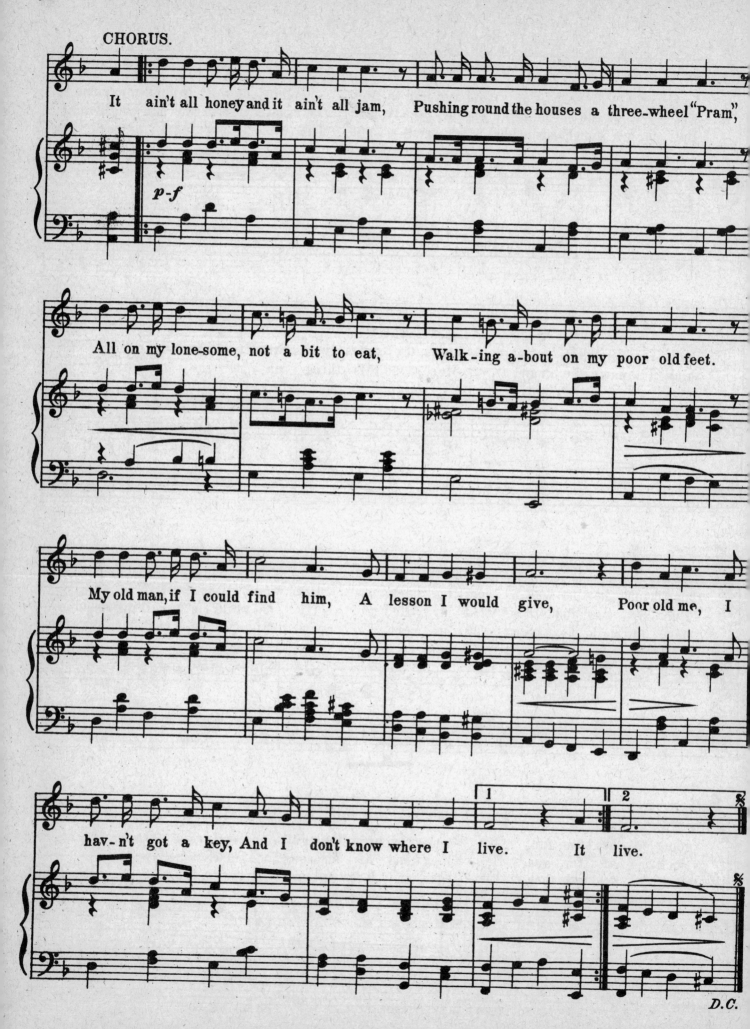

It ain't all honey and it ain't all jam, Pushing round the houses a three-wheel "Pram",

*p-f*

All on my lone-some, not a bit to eat, Walk-ing a-bout on my poor old feet.

My old man, if I could find him, A lesson I would give, Poor old me, I

hav-n't got a key, And I don't know where I live. It live.

*D.C.*

# Molly O!

WM. J. SCANLAN

Bright Waltz Tempo

She's plain Mol - ly O, \_\_\_\_\_ sim - ple and sweet, \_\_\_
Brave sol - diers may war, \_\_\_\_\_ he - roes may die, \_\_\_

My heart is gone, \_\_\_ I lay me at her feet; \_\_\_
With Mol - ly, dear, \_\_\_ the world I would de - fy; \_\_\_

So light her tread, \_\_\_ so fond her gaze, \_\_\_
Ten - der her heart, \_\_\_ lov - ing and true, \_\_\_

Who would not love my Mol - ly dear? \_\_\_\_\_
Flow'rs of the val - ley call her queen! \_\_\_\_\_

*Arr. by Hugo Frey*

Clouds ___ are but sun - shine, skies ___ ev-er
So ___ like the lil - y, so ___ like the

clear, ___ Hap - py am I, lads, when Mol-ly ___ is
rose ___ Her ___ laugh's like sun - shine to na-ture's ___ re-

near; ___ Heart's ___ fond-est ech-o, ___ Love's ___ sweet re-
pose; ___ Her ___ eyes are jew-els, ___ more ___ rich and

frain ___ Still ___ call me back ___ to my Mol - ly a-gain! ___
bright ___ Than ___ those in Heav - en that spark - le at night!

Chorus, Bright Waltz Tempo

She's plain Mol - ly O, \_\_\_\_\_ sim - ple and

sweet, \_\_\_\_\_ She's plain Mol - ly O, \_\_\_\_\_ her heart is

love's re - treat, \_\_\_\_\_ She's plain Mol - ly O! \_\_\_\_\_

love - ly, di - vine, \_\_\_\_\_ Oh, would that I \_\_\_\_\_

\_\_ could call Mol - ly mine! She's mine! \_\_\_\_\_

# Mother, Pin A Rose On Me

PAUL SCHINDLER
DAVE LEWIS
BOB ADAMS

Moderately bright

I love the coun-try air, I love the sum-mer
I trav-eled all a - round, To New York for a

time, I love to lin-ger in the shade or bask in the old sun - shine. I
lark, I went to sleep up-on a bench out in Cen-tral Park, But

nev - er bor-row trou-ble, as long as I eat, you see, For
soon I was a - wak-ened, was fun-ny don't you see, It

ev-'ry day is Sun-day, they all look a-like to me.
looked like a coun-try or - chard, a "pear" be - neath each tree.

*Arr. by Hugo Frey*

Copyright 1942 **ROBBINS MUSIC CORPORATION**, 799 Seventh Ave., New York, N. Y.

Chorus, Snappy

# Not So Long Ago

Words and Music by
ROSE MONROE

Moderato espressivo.

Tell me why you turn a - way so sad - ly, One must
All I ask is just one smile of glad - ness, Just one

not be - lieve all that one hears,_____ In your
ray of hope for my lone heart,_____ Do not

heart you know I love you mad - ly, Must I
let me lin - ger in my sad - ness, Do not

joys a dream of yes - ter - day?
did, dear not so long a - go!

**CHORUS.**

Not so long a-go, you seemed to miss me, Not so

long a-go, you loved me so, Not so

long a-go, you yearned to kiss me, And you were

# There Is A Tavern In The Town
## (Fare-Thee-Well, For I Must Leave Thee)

Arranged by
TED FIORITO

Moderato (*Moderately*)

There Is A Tav-ern In The Town, in the town, And
He left me for a dam-sel dark, dam-sel dark, Each
Oh! dig my grave both wide and deep, wide and deep, Put

there my dear love sits him down, sits him down, And_ drinks his wine 'mid
Fri_day night they used to spark, used to spark, And_ now my love, once
tomb-stones at my head and feet, head and feet,_ And_ on my breast carve a

laugh-ter_ free, And nev-er, nev-er thinks of me.
true to_ me, Takes that dark dam-sel on his knee.
tur-tle_ dove, To sig-ni-fy I died of love.

*Transcription by Hugo Frey*

# The Man On The Flying Trapeze

By WALTER O'KEEF

Valse moderato

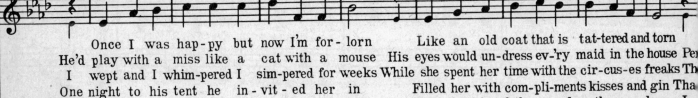

Once I was hap-py but now I'm for-lorn    Like an old coat that is tat-tered and torn
He'd play with a miss like a cat with a mouse His eyes would un-dress ev-'ry maid in the house Per
I wept and I whim-pered I sim-pered for weeks While she spent her time with the cir-cus-es freaks Th
One night to his tent he in-vit-ed her in    Filled her with com-pli-ments kisses and gin Tha
One night I as u-sual went to her dear home    Found there her fath-er and moth-er a-lone I
Some months af-ter that I went in-to a hall    To my sur-prise I found there on the wall A

Left in this wide world to weep and to mourn Be-trayed by a maid in her teens.___ Oh, thi
haps he is bet-ter de-scribed as a louse But still peo-ple came just the same.___ He'd
tears were like hail-stones that rolled down my cheeks A-las and a-lack and a-las-ka.___ I
start-ed her off on the road to roo-in She made the su-preme sac-ri-fice.___ But
asked for my love___ and soon t'was made known To my hor-ror that she'd run a-way___ With
bill in red let-ters which did my heart gall That she was ap-pear-ing with him___ He'd

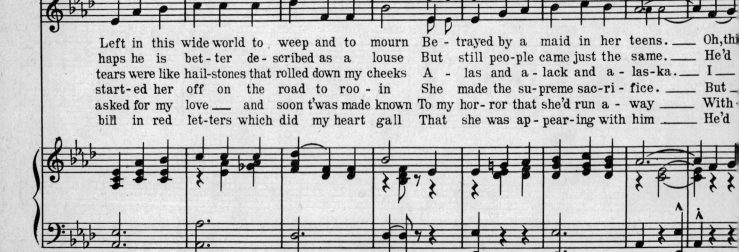

# The Bearded Lady

WALTER O'KEEFE

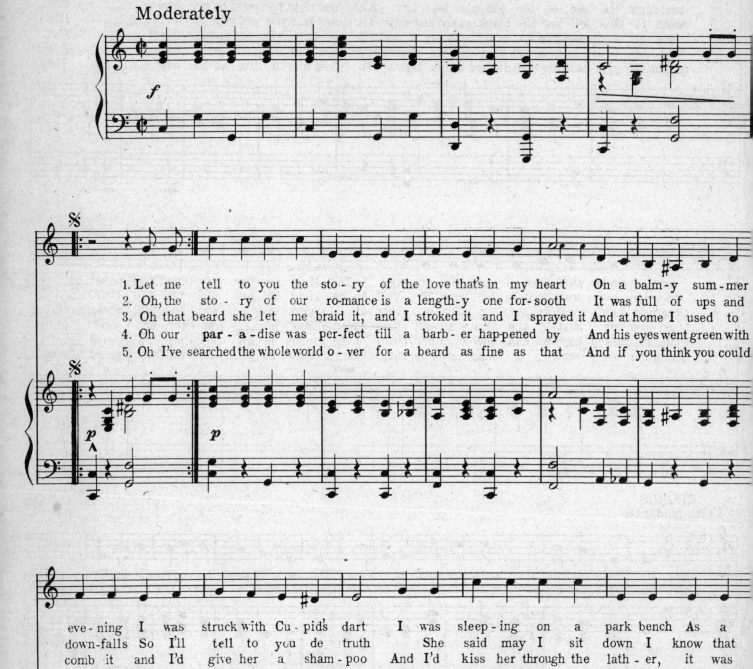

1. Let me tell to you the sto-ry of the love that's in my heart On a balm-y sum-mer
2. Oh, the sto-ry of our ro-mance is a length-y one for-sooth It was full of ups and
3. Oh that beard she let me braid it, and I stroked it and I sprayed it And at home I used to
4. Oh our **par-a**-dise was per-fect till a barb-er hap-pened by And his eyes went green with
5. Oh I've searched the whole world o-ver for a beard as fine as that And if you think you could

eve-ning I was struck with Cu-pid's dart I was sleep-ing on a park bench As a
down-falls So I'll tell to you de truth She said may I sit down I know that
comb it and I'd give her a sham-poo And I'd kiss her through the lath-er, it was
en-vy as her whis-kers caught his eye Oh this god-dess that I wor-shipped has de-
find one then you're talk-ing thru your hat So if you should see a Beard-ed La-dy

rall.

wind blew thru the trees When a wom - an turned the cor - ner with a beard down to her knees. I
some men might have jeered But_ I po - lite - ly said, "Why No!" Sit down and rest your beard! I
pleas - ant both - er rath - er Such con - duct might seem strange but_ broth - er would - n't you? I
vel - oped feet of clay He_ shaved her once, she liked it, Now she shaves three times a day. I
please re - mem - ber me And_ have her call me up some time at Maine 6 9 5 3 I

rall.

Chorus, Moderately

Love The Beard-ed La - dy 'cause her kiss - es tick - le so Her whis-kers make me prick - le From my

mp

head down to my toe Oh that kiss with the mus-tache in it No won-der I get

pas - sion-ate I love The Beard - ed La - dy 'cause her whis-kers tick - le so.

D.S.

mf

sfz D.S.

# The Gambler's Wife

WALTER O'KEEFE

case of a man Who _ squan-ders his mon - ey and gam-bles _____ It's _____ his great big
tucked up his sleeve Mc _ Snish made a clean up, a kill - ing _____ So they start-ed to
Mis - sus Mc Snish The _ God-dess of chance is so fick - le _____ You _ know how it

vice to play hors - es or dice And _ that makes his home life a sham-bles. Oh!
throw a - way _ all of his dough And O - phel - ia the dum-bell was will - ing. Oh!
goes, you just _ pay through the nose And you nev - er wind up with a nick - el. Oh!

**Refrain**

Pit - y the life of a Gam-bler's Wife Just think of the mon-ey that's spent, _____ One

day she's a queen In a grand li - mou-sine And the next day she ain't got a cent. _____

D.C.

# Always A Bridesmaid
## (But Never A Bride)

WALTER O'KEEFE

Moderate waltz time

1. I once knew a spin-ster who worked on a plan To get her a hus-band, she want-ed a man She dressed like a flap-per and lift-ed her pan. She__ hoped that she'd soon be a bride._____ Mae__ West was her mod-el, she
2. Her feet were like Gar-bo's, her nose like Du-rante's She dressed up like Diet-rich with two pair of pants But she could-n't mar-ry there was-n't a chance. She was more like a mo-ther, you see._____ Then one day a sales-man came
3. Now he was a bound-er, a beast and a cur And he made a ter-ri-ble chump out of her He said to her "Hon-ey! it's you I pre-fer." Just__ leave ev'-ry-thing up to me._____ So she went to the bank and she

°D7    G    °D7    G    A7

cop-ied her stuff But she was too skin-ny, not bux-om e-nough She just could-n't
in-to her life It looked as if she'd be his strug-gle and strife But then he re-
op-ened the box; She gave him her dia-monds, her bonds and her stocks And when he left

°D    dim.    °D    A7    °D    °D7

take it when fel-lows got tough So she let down her hair and she cried, Oh!
mem-bered that he had a wife And she said "Please take pit-y on me." Oh!
town she was high on the rocks And now she is luck-y to be. Oh!

**Refrain** G    A7    °D7    G

*mf*

Al-ways A Brides-maid but nev-er a bride My lov-ers leave me in the lurch.___ He

A7    °D7    G

must have de-ceived me 'cause here I am now Hang-ing a-round at the church.___ *D.C.*

# The Tattooed Lady

WALTER O'KEEFE

Moderato Valse Tempo

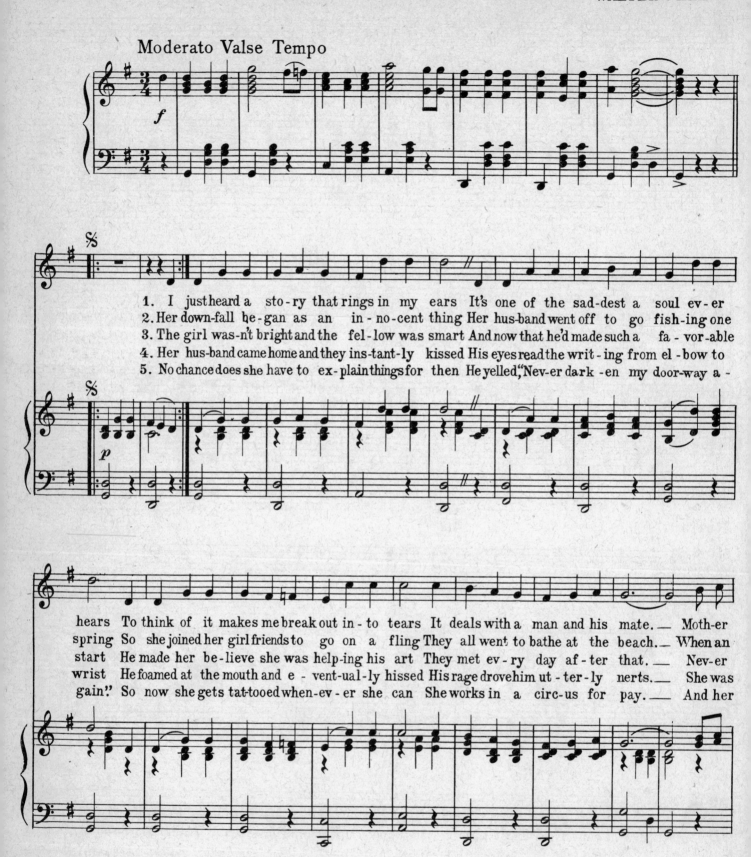

1. I just heard a sto-ry that rings in my ears It's one of the sad-dest a soul ev-er
2. Her down-fall be-gan as an in-no-cent thing Her hus-band went off to go fish-ing one
3. The girl was-n't bright and the fel-low was smart And now that he'd made such a fa-vor-able
4. Her hus-band came home and they ins-tant-ly kissed His eyes read the writ-ing from el-bow to
5. No chance does she have to ex-plain things for then He yelled,"Nev-er dark-en my door-way a-

hears To think of it makes me break out in-to tears It deals with a man and his mate.— Moth-er
spring So she joined her girl friends to go on a fling They all went to bathe at the beach.— When an
start He made her be-lieve she was help-ing his art They met ev-ry day af-ter that.— Nev-er
wrist He foamed at the mouth and e-vent-ual-ly hissed His rage drove him ut-ter-ly nerts.— She was
gain." So now she gets tat-tooed when-ev-er she can She works in a circ-us for pay.— And her

Eve in the gar-den of E - den ___ Heard the ser-pent the same as this lass ___ And this
art - ist came up with his paint pot ___ She thought she'd lead him on for a laugh ___ But the
once did she think that he loved her ___ Nor did she think that he'd do her harm ___ Till the
hurt by his at - ti - tude deep-ly ___ And hys-ter-ic'-lly start-ed to laugh ___ As she
love - ly white skin is now paint-ed ___ With the pic-tures of sail-ors and such ___ If you

girl might have turned from temp-ta - tion ex - cept For a ter - ri - ble snake in the grass. Oh!
blight - er tat-tooed on her shoul-der a fiend Who was saw - ing a wom-an in half. Oh!
day that he tat-tooed in red white and blue And he wrote,"I love you"on her arm. Oh!
shrugged her left shoul-der he no-ticed the beast Who was saw - ing the wom-an in half! Oh!
pay her a quar-ter you too can tat - too On the skin that you'd once love to touch. Oh!

Chorus

Shame on the man who pur-sued her ___ The vil-lain who vic-ious-ly wooed her ___ She

fell in a faint so he sent for his paint And the first thing she knew he tat-tooed her! ___

D.S.

D.S.

# Father Put The Cow Away

WALTER O'KEEFE

Moderately

Poor Ez - ra sat on the milk - ing stool, The cow sat down be - side him, The
You heard those vil - lage___ bells to - night They're ring - ing out for Har - ry, And
To - night's their wed - ding___ night pa - pa, And all my dreams are dead now I

cow had noth - ing else to do, With no one there to guide him While
Ma - ry is his prom - ised bride The gal I was to mar - ry She
have no hopes no fu - ture So I think I'll go to bed now. I

Ez - ra cried and cried and cried The sobs were shak - ing thru him He
was my fi - an - cee un - til He made her break her prom - ise. So
used to think I'd mar - ry and Like you I'd be a fa - ther But

called his fa - ther ov - er and In tears he then said to him:
now I think I'll go up - stairs And put on my pa - ja - mas:
now I've lost my in - t'rest Pop, I would - n't want to both - er:

## Refrain

Oh! Fa-ther Put The Cow A -way And get it out of sight Cause I am heav-y

heart - ed And I can-not milk to - night It is - n't fair to this here cow For

me to try to milk her now So Fa-ther Put The Cow A-way I can-not milk to - night.

# "Bully" Song

Words and Music by
CHARLES E. TREVATHAN

Arr. by Hugo Frey

# Frankie And Johnny

Transcription by
HUGO FREY

5. Ain't gon-na tell you no stor-y Ain't gon-na tell you no lie But your
6. Frank-ie went home in a hur-ry She did-n't go there for fun She
7. She took a cab at the cor-ner Says"Driv-er Step on this can" Oh!
8. Frank-ie got out on South Clark Street And thru a win-dow so high Saw

John-ny went by a-bout an hour a-go With a girl named Nel-lie Blye. He was her
hur-ried home to get a hold of her John-ny's shoot-in' gun. He was her
she was a des-p'rate wo-man Get-tin' two-timed by her man. He was her
John-ny her man a lov-in' up That high brown Nel-lie Blye. He was her

man_____ but he done her wrong._____
man_____ but he done her wrong._____
man_____ but he done her wrong._____
man_____ but he done her wrong._____

Guitar tacit

9. John-ny saw Frank-ie a com-in'   Out the back door he did   scoot   But
10. Bring out your long black cof-fin   Bring out your fun - er - al   clothes   My
11. Drive out your rub - ber tired car-riage   Drive out your rub - ber tired   hack   There's
12. Sher-iff ar - rest - ed poor Frank-ie   Took her to jail that same   day   He

Frank-ie took aim with her pis - tol   And the gun went root-a-toot-toot, He was her
John-ny's gone and cashed his bad   checks   To the grave-yard John - ny goes   He was her
twelve men a - go-ing to the grave - yard   And e - lev - en com - ing back   He was her
locked her up in a dung-eon cell   And threw the key a - way, He was her

man but he done her wrong.
man but he done her wrong.
man but he done her wrong.
man but he done her wrong.

# Any Rags?

THOMAS S. ALLEN

*Arr. by Hugo Frey*

rags, an-y bones, an-y bot-tles to-day, there's a great big rag pick-er

com-ing this way, "An-y rags?" "Rags?"

An-y rags, an-y bones, an-y bot-tles to-day, it's the

same old sto-ry, in the same old way. If you same old way.

D.S. 𝄋 *Fine*

*Fine*

# Bill Bailey, Won't You Please Come Home?

Words and Music by
HUGHIE CANNON

anscription by HUGO FREY

# Chorus
### Moderato (well accentuated)

Won't you come home, Bill Bai - ley, Won't You Come Home?   She moans the whole day

long; _____   I'll do de cook-ing, dar - ling I'll pay de rent,   I knows I've

done you wrong. _____   'Mem-ber dat rain - y eve dat I drove you out,   Wid

noth - in' but a fine tooth comb? _____   I knows I'se to blame, well, ain't dat a

shame? Bill Bai - ley, Won't You Please Come Home? _____   Home? _____

# The Spider And The Fly

Words by
**ARTHUR J. LAMB**

Music by
HARRY VON TILZER

Moderate Waltz tempo

"Kiss me good-night moth-er dar - ling, Why are you sad to - night?
Roam-ing a - lone thro' the cit - y Just at the twi - light's fall,

Soon I will dance with the man I love, In the ball-room so bright"
Left all a - lone by the man she wed, Whom she'd loved best of all,

Fond-ly her moth-er em-braced her Say-ing "My dear do not go,
Clasp-ing her ba - by still clos - er Weep-ing she now bows her head,

*Arr. by Hugo Frey*

I have warned you a-gainst his love, And now dear, my rea-son you'll know."

As she kneels by her moth-er's grave, And thinks of the words that she said.

**Chorus, Moderately** (*with expression*)

"Think of the spi-der, a man so false, And the fly a maid-en fair,

Think of him lead-ing her step by step, In-to his cru-el snare.

Think of a love that is worse than hate, Don't let the les-son go by_____ But

stop ere too late, And don't share the fate of the spi-der and the fly."

# Lam', Lam', Lam'

Words by
**FRANK ABBOTT**

Music by
**BEN M. JEROME**

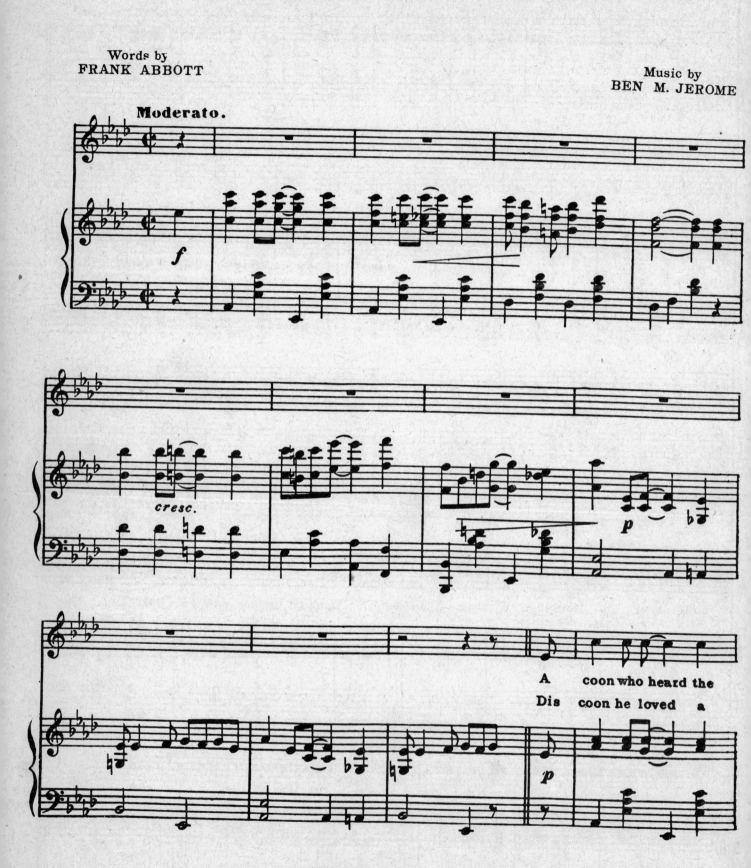

A coon who heard the
Dis coon he loved a

Published by **ROBBINS MUSIC CORPORATION**, 799 Seventh Ave., New York, N. Y.

prais - es sung of chicken on ev - 'ry side ___ He got ex - cited and
yal - ler maid who's name was Lu - cin - dy Lamb ___ Her fa - ther kept a

den he got so mad he al - most cried, ___ Says he I think dis
butcher - shop and he took a dis - like to Sam, ___ Says he "now coon keep a

chick - en craze is a li - bel on de col - ored race ___ A
way from my house my child you can - not wed ___ Then

man dont have to be stuck on fowl just be - cause he's black in de face ___
Sam gave him one sheepish look and to the butcher said ___

I know lots of coons, cra-zy as loons, eat chick-en day and night, __ But
Dere is lots of gals, Suzies and Sals and Man-dys by de score, __ Dat

as for me I can't a-gree my tastes are the same as white __ I
I could wed but on de dead Lu - cin - dy I a - dore __ I

don't go back on can-vas back, I'm fond of Lit-tle neck clams __ But my
don't care a rap for your butcher shop, for your beef, pork, veal or ham, __ But I'll

fav-or-ite flesh I must con-fess is Lam', Lam', Lam', __
win ma flame cause I likes her name it's Lam', Lam', Lam', __

CHORUS.

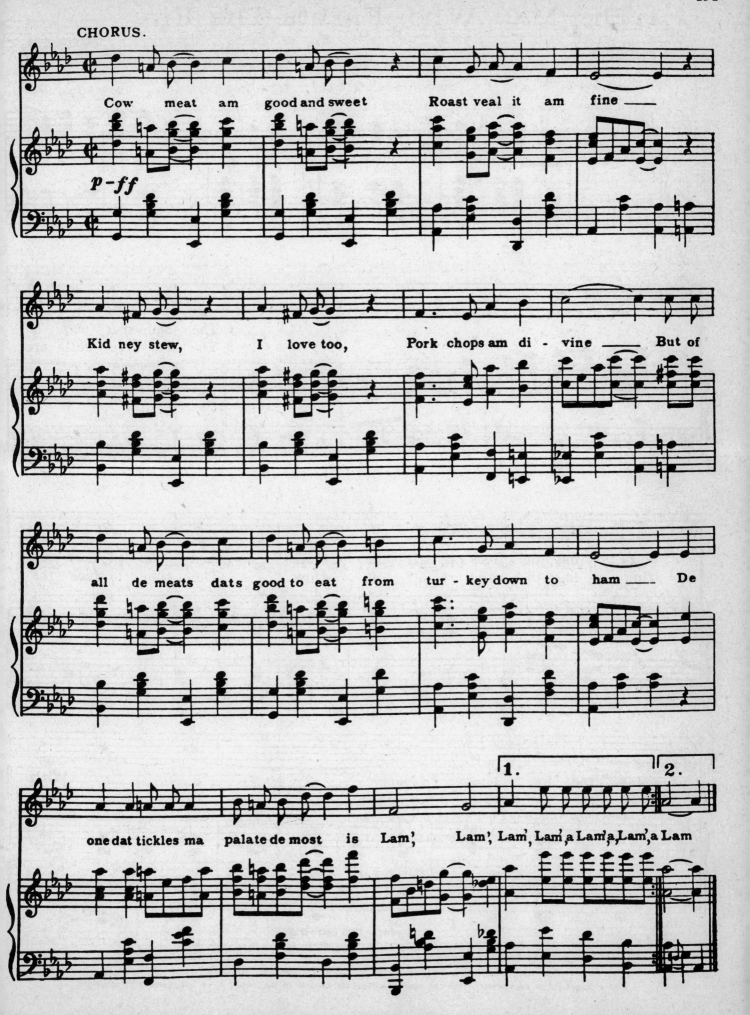

Cow meat am good and sweet Roast veal it am fine ____

Kid ney stew, I love too, Pork chops am di - vine ____ But of

all de meats dats good to eat from tur - key down to ham ____ De

one dat tickles ma palate de most is Lam', Lam', Lam', Lam', a Lam' a, Lam', a Lam

# The Man Who Fights The Fire

Words by
**FELIX F. FEIST**

Music by
**JOS. S. NATHAN**

1. The sum-mer sun is beam-ing the trees are all in bloom ___ And hap-pi-ness sur-rounds the co-sy home. ___ With

2. The fi-re bells are ring-ing the skies are all a-glow, ___ The time to face the fran-tic foe is nigh. ___ The

child - ren 'round a - play - ing there is - n't 'room for gloom: The
win - ter winds are sing - ing as off to fight they go, The

faith - ful fath - er lit - tle cares to roam; _____ He's
fi - re chiefs' com - mands are heard on high; _____ With

al - ways light and gay un - til du - ty calls him 'way \_\_\_ And
lad - der and with hose each he - ro brave - ly goes \_\_\_ To

as the shades of night be - gin to fall; _____ He
face a foe that fears no hu - man hand; _____ But

leaves them with a sigh,—— he goes per-haps to die;—— Yet
he is fear-less too,—— and when the bat-tle's through,—— The

staunch and true he an-swers du-ty's call.——
vic - to - ry he's won is might-y grand.——

**CHORUS**

He's the man who fights the smoke, the flames and fire,———— No brav-er man the

count-ry ev-er knew;———— When dan - ger's near,—— he

# Only One Girl In The World For Me

DAVE MARION

Bright Waltz tempo

Ballad style

There's on - ly one girl in the world that I would call my wife,
My sweet-heart is an or - phan, and I'm a work-ing lad,

And the girl I sing of, I love dear - er than my life, My
But if work was stead - y, why it would not be so bad, We've

sweet-heart's age is just eigh - teen, she greets me with a smile, And
been en - gaged a - bout one year, and last night at the gate, She

Arr. by Hugo Frey

when she says good eve-ning dear, I'm think-ing all the while, That there is
said as tears came to her eyes, "My own true love I'll wait." So there is

**Chorus, Moderate Waltz tempo**

On - ly one girl in the world for me, _____

on - ly one girl has my sym-pa-thy, _____ She's

not so ver-y pret-ty, _____ nor of a high de-gree, _____ There's on -

ly one girl in the world for me. _____ me. _____

# Absence Makes The Heart Grow Fonder

Words by
**ARTHUR GILLESPIE**

Music by
**HERBERT DILLEA**

Slowly (*with expression*)

Sweet-heart I have grown so lone-ly, Liv-ing thus a-way from you,
Has the love that once was dear-er Than all else to me grown cold?

For I love you and you on-ly; Still I won-der if you're true
Or has ab-sence drawn us near-er, To each oth-er as of old?

I re-gret the harsh words spo-ken, That I know have caused you pain,
Prom-ise then you will not sev-er, From the ties that bind us two.

And my heart is near-ly bro-ken, Say you love me once a-gain.
Say you will be mine for-ev-er, Tell me that you still are true.

Arr. by Hugo Frey

Chorus, Slowly (*with expression*)

Ab-sence makes the heart grow fond - er, That is why I long for you; —

Lone-ly thro' the nights I pon - der, Wond-'ring dar - ling, if you're true —

Dis-tance on - ly lends en - chant - ment. Tho' the o - cean waves di - vide, —

Ab - sence makes the heart grow fond - er, Long-ing to be near your side. —

# The Mansion Of Aching Hearts

Words by
ARTHUR J. LAMB

Music by
HARRY VON TILZER

*Arr. by Hugo Frey*

Chorus, Slowly *(with expression)*

# She May Have Seen Better Days

JAMES THORNTON

Slowly, Ballad style

Slowly, Ballad style

While stroll-ing a - long with the cit-y's vast throng, On a night that was bit-ter-ly
If we could but tell why the poor crea-ture fell, Per - haps we'd be not so se-
The crowd went a - way, But I long-er did stay, For from her I was loathe to de-

cold, _____ I no - ticed a crowd who were laugh-ing a - loud At
vere; _____ If the truth were but known, Of this out - cast a - lone, May-
part; _____ I knew by her moan, As she sat there a - lone, That

some-thing they chanc'd to be - hold. _____ I stopped for to see What the ob - ject could
hap we would all shed a tear; _____ She was once some - one's joy, Cast a - side like a
some-thing was break - ing her heart; _____ She told me her life, She was once a good

*Arr. by Hugo Frey*

be, And there, on a door-step, lay___ A wo-man in tears from the
toy, A-ban-doned, for-sak-en, un-known;___ Ev'ry man stand-ing by had a
wife, Re-spect-ed and hon-ored by all;___ Her hus-band had fled, Ere_

*rall.*

crowd's an-gry jeers; And then I heard some-bod-y say:___
tear in his eye, For some had a daugh-ter at home.___
they were long wed, And tears down her cheeks sad-ly fall.___

*rall.*

Slowly

She May Have Seen Bet-ter Days, ___ When she was in her prime; ___ She May Have Seen Bet-ter

*mf*

Days, ___ Once up-on a time. ___ Tho' by the way-side she fell, ___ She may

yet mend her ways, ___ Some poor old moth-er is wait-ing for her, Who has seen bet-ter days. ___

# I'm Sorry I Made You Cry

By N. J. CLESI
*Arr. by Theodore Morse*

won't you for - give? Don't let us say good - bye!

One lit - tle word,____ one lit - tle smile,____ One lit - tle

kiss, wont you try?____ It breaks my heart to hear you

sigh, I'm sor - ry I made you cry!____ cry!___

# The Quilting Party

Slowly

In the sky the bright stars glit-tered, On the bank the pale moon shone; And 'twas
On my arm a soft hand rest-ed, Rest-ed light as o-cean foam; And 'twas
On my lips a whis-per trem-bled, Trem-bled till it dared to come; And 'twas
On my life new hopes were dawn-ing, And those hopes have liv'd and grown; And 'twas

from Aunt Di-nah's quilt-ing par-ty, I was see-ing Nel-lie home.
from Aunt Di-nah's quilt-ing par-ty, I was see-ing Nel-lie home.
from Aunt Di-nah's quilt-ing par-ty, I was see-ing Nel-lie home.
from Aunt Di-nah's quilt-ing par-ty, I was see-ing Nel-lie home.

Chorus

I was see-ing Nel-lie home,_ I was see-ing Nel-lie home; And 'twas

from Aunt Di-nah's quilt-ing par-ty, I was see-ing Nel-lie home.

Robbins Music Corporation, New York, N. Y.

# And Her Golden Hair Was Hanging Down Her Back

By FELIX MC GLENNON
and MONROE H. ROSENFELL

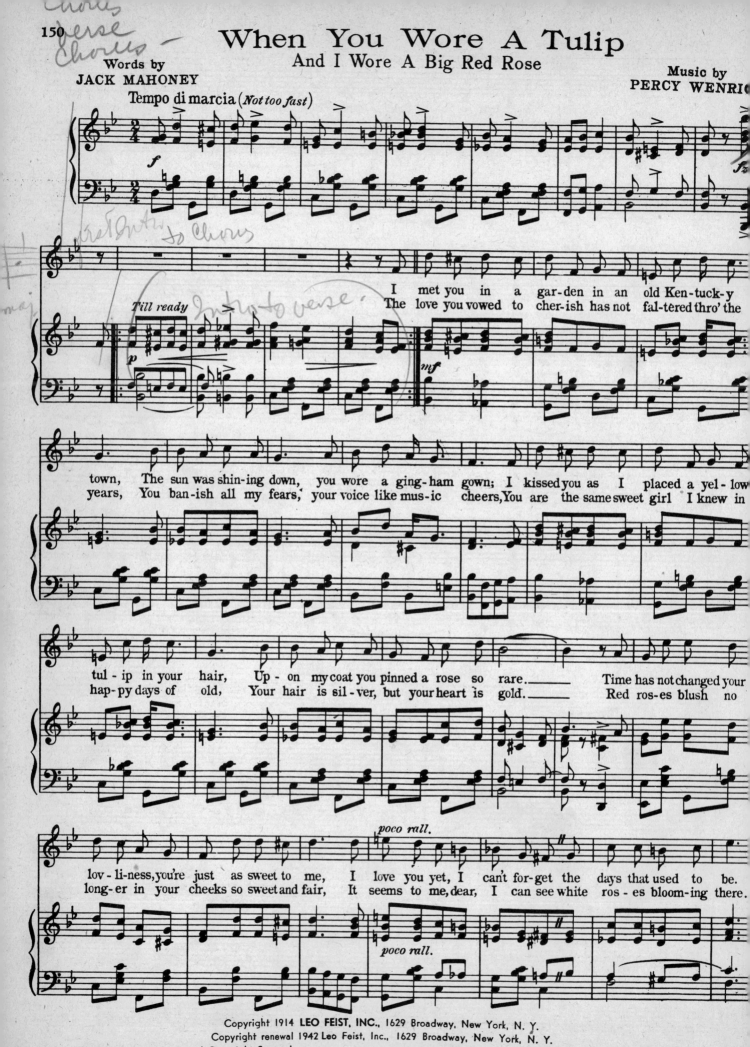

# Li'l Liza Jane

Words and Music by
Countess Ada De Lachau

# Peek-A-Boo

Words and Music by
WM. J. SCANLON

On a cold win-ter's ev-'ning, when bus-'ness is done,
Oh, my heart's al-ways light when at home with my wife,
When the sun-shine of youth fades, and age sends us low,

And to your home you re-tire,_____ What a
There joy and peace ev-er reign;_____ With my
Joys, like the birds, flown a-way;_____ Then the

plea-sure it is to have a bright bounc-ing boy,
boy on my knee___ I'm as hap-py as can be,
smiles of our child-ren ev-er bright-en the path,

*Arr. by Hugo Frey*

One whom you love to ad - mire; _____ You hug him, and kiss him, you
I nev - er knew care or pain; _____ He's pret - ty, he's gen - tle, he's
Lead - ing where loved ones do stray. _____ The mu - sic and laugh - ter we

press him to your heart, What joy to your bo - som 'twill
kind and he is good, And ev - 'ry - thing nice, him I
ev - er love to hear, Will beam like a rain - bow in

bring; _____ Then you place him on the car - pet, And you'll
bring; _____ Oh, if he at - tempts to cry _____ When _____
spring; _____ By the fire - side at night, _____ With our

Waltz tempo

hide be - hind the chair, And to please him you'll com - mence to sing: _____
I am stand - ing by, Just to please him I com - mence to sing: _____
hearts so free and light, We will lis - ten while our chil - dren sing: _____

Chorus, Waltz tempo

Peek - a - boo! peek - a - boo! Come from be -
hind the chair; _____ Peek - a -
boo! peek - a - boo! I see you hid - ing
there, Oh! you ras - cal. there. _____

1.

2.

# She Is More To Be Pitied Than Censured

WILLIAM GRAY

Moderate Waltz tempo

Moderate Waltz tempo

At the old con-cert hall on the Bow-'ry____ 'Round a ta-ble were
There's an old fash-ioned church 'round the cor-ner,____ Where the neigh-bors all

seat-ed one night,____ A crowd of young fel-lows ca-rous-ing,____
gath-ered one day,____ While the par-son was preach-ing a ser-mon,____

— With them life seemed cheer-ful and bright,____ At the
— O'er a soul that had just passed a-way,____ 'Twas this

Arr. by Hugo Frey

next ta - ble some one was seat - ed, \_\_\_\_\_ A girl who had
same way - ward girl from the Bow - 'ry \_\_\_\_\_ Who a life of ad -

fall - en to shame, \_\_\_\_\_ All the young fel - lows jeered at her
ven - ture had led, \_\_\_\_\_ Did the cler - gy - man jeer at her

weak - ness, \_\_\_\_\_ 'Till they heard an old wom - an ex - claim; \_\_\_\_\_
down - fall? \_\_\_\_\_ No, he asked for God's mer - cy and said; \_\_\_\_\_

**Chorus, Moderate Waltz tempo**

She is more to be pit - ied than cen - sured, \_\_\_\_\_ She is more to be

helped than de - spised,_____ She is on - ly a las-sie who ven - tured,_____ On

life's storm-y path ill ad - vised,_____ Do not scorn her with words fierce and bit - ter,_____

_____ Do not laugh at her shame and down - fall,_____ For a mo-ment just

stop and con - sid - er,_____ That a man was the cause of it all._____

*rall.*

# There's A Big Cry Baby In The Moon

Words and Music by
BRYMN, SMITH & BURRIS

I have stud-ied all the stars, I know ev-'ry-thing 'bout Mars, I have
Sure as two and one are three, No one knows 'bout this but me, It's a

e-ven lec-tur'd on Moon-òl-o-gy ——— Now some of our great-est men I ad-
se-cret, but I'll tell it just the same,——— Now some folks ac-cuse the moon for not

vise them now and then; of course my name's not down in his-to-ry ——— Just what
shin-ing when they spoon; But poor old moon is not at all to blame ——— When you

caus - es rain to fall and the real cause of it all, I'm the
see the clouds a - rise, there's a pair of tear dimmed eyes, It's the

on - ly per-son knows how to ex - plain, ___ And I cert'n-ly have the proof and I
babe up there who's fret-ful as can be, ___ And it will not go to sleep pret - ty

know that it's the truth; Here's the rea-son why, some-times that we have rain.
soon be-gins to weep; So you see just why it rains on you and me.

mf L.H.

**Chorus, Moderato**

There's a big cry ba - by in the moon, moon, moon, that cries, cries,

p-f

cries,　When the rain am pour - ing, It's the tears am fall - ing from his

eyes,　eyes,　eyes.　When you hear it thun-der ei - ther night or noon, that's a

might - y sure sign__ he's goin' to cry out soon,__ That's why I say__ there's a

big cry ba - by in the moon,　moon,　moon.__ There's a　moon.__

# Hail! Hail! The Gang's All Here!
### (What The deuce Do We Care)

Words by
**D. A. ESROM**

Music by
**THEODORE MORSE**
**ARTHUR SULLIVAN**

# Silver Threads Among The Gold

**Words by**
**EBEN E. REXFORD**

**Music by**
**H. P. DANKS**

Andante con Espressione

1. Dar-ling, I am grow-ing old, _____ Sil-ver Threads A-mong The Gold,
2. When your hair is sil-ver white, _____ And your cheeks no lon-ger bright,
3. Love can nev-er more grow old, _____ Locks may lose their brown and gold,
4. Love is al-ways young and fair, _____ What to us is sil-ver hair,

Shine up-on my brow to-day, _____ Life is fad-ing fast a-way;
With the ros-es of the May, _____ I will kiss your lips and say;
Cheeks may fade and hol-low grow, _____ But the hearts that love will know;
Fad-ed cheeks or steps grown slow, _____ To the hearts that beat be-low?

But, my dar-ling you will be, will be,
Oh! my dar-ling mine a-lone, a-lone,
Nev-er, nev-er win-ter's frost and chill,
Since I kissed you, mine a-lone, a-lone,

Al-ways young and fair to me, ____
You have nev-er old-er grown, ____
Sum-mer warmth is in them still, ____
You have nev-er old-er grown, ____

Yes, my dar-ling you will be, ____
Yes, my dar-ling mine a-lone, ____
Nev-er win-ter's frost and chill, ____
Since I kissed you, mine a-lone, ____

Al-ways young and fair to me. ____
You have nev-er old-er grown. ____
Sum-mer warmth is in them still. ____
You have nev-er old-er grown. ____

Refrain

Dar-ling, I am grow-ing, grow-ing old,  Sil-ver Threads A-mong The Gold, ____

Shine up-on my brow to-day, ____  Life is fad-ing fast a-way. ____

# The Spanish Cavalier

Words and Music by
W. D. HENDRICKSON

Robbins Music Corporation, New York, N. Y.

# When The Robins Nest Again

FRANK HOWARD

# The Musket Or The Sword

Words by
CARROLL FLEMING

Music by
ROBT. A. KEISER

**Tempo di Marcia.**

long   a cit - y pave-ment while   the   crowd was surg - ing by,   Two
mid   the bat - tle's fier-cest strife,   the   pri - vate fought his way,   And

sol - diers hur-ried to-ward   a man - sion   grand,_____   The
when the Col - onel turned   in fear   and   fled,_____   The

LEO FEIST, INC., 1629 Broadway, New York, N. Y.

call "to arms" had sound - ed and they each had come to try, And
brave com-mand - er said, "my lad 'twas you who saved the day," And

gain a maid - en's prom - ise of her hand.\_\_\_\_\_ She
you are now a Col - onel in his stead.\_\_\_\_\_ So

was a sol - dier's daugh-ter,\_ and her heart was beat - ing high, When
when the war was o - ver\_ and the sol - dier boys came back, The

she was asked to be a Col - onel's bride,\_\_\_\_ The
he - ro and the maid - en met once more,\_\_\_\_ This

172

all he could af - ford, _____ The Col - onel, old and
wealth - y, _____ had of - fered gold and fame, _____ Which should she
choose, which one re - fuse, The musk-et or the sword. _____ One
sword. _____

D.S.

# We Never Speak As We Pass By

Words and Music by
H. MILFORD

Moderately slow

The spell has passed, the dream is o'er, And tho' we meet, we have no
In guile-less youth I sought her side, And she be-came my vir-tuous
In gild-ed Hall 'midst wealth she dwells, How her heart aches, her sad face

more, One heart is crushed to droop and die, And for re-
bride, Our lot was peace, so fair, so bright, One sun-ny
tells, She fain would smile, seem bright and gay, But con-science

lief must Heav'n-ward fly; The once bright smile has fad-ed,
day, no gloom-y night; No life on earth more pure than
steals her peace a-way; And when the flat-t'rer casts a-

gone, And giv-en way to looks for-lorn, De-spite her
ours, In that dear home, 'midst fields and flow'rs, Un-til the
side, My fall-en and dis-hon-ored bride, I'll close her

*Arr. by Hugo Frey*    Copyright 1942 ROBBINS MUSIC CORPORATION, 799 Seventh Ave., New York, N.Y.

gran - deur, wick - ed fame, She stoops to blush be - neath her shame.
tempt - er came to Nell, It daz - zled her, a - las she fell! —
eyes in death for - give And in my heart, her name shall live. —

**Chorus, Slowly**

We nev - er speak as we pass by, Al - tho' a

tear be - dims her eye, I know she thinks of her past

life, When we were lov - ing man and wife. — —

# A Boy's Best Friend Is His Mother

Words by
**HARRY MILLER**

Music by
**J. P. SKELLY**

While plod-ding on our way, the toil-some road of life, How few the friends that dai-ly there we meet! — Not man-y will stand by in troub-le and in strife, With coun-sel and af-fec-tion ev-er sweet! — But there is one whose smile, will

Tho' all the world may frown, and ev-'ry friend de-part, She nev-er will for-sake us in our need! — Our re-fuge ev-er-more is still with-in her heart, For us her lov-ing sym-pa-thy will plead! — Her pure and gen-tle smile, for

Her fond and gen-tle face not long may greet us here, Then cheer her with our kind-ness and our love! — Re-mem-ber at her knee in child-hood bright and dear, We heard her voice, like an-gel's from a - bove! — Tho' af - ter years may bring, their

*Arr. by Hugo Frey*

# If We Can't Be The Same Old Sweethearts
# We'll Just Be The Same Old Friends

Words by
JOE McCARTHY

Music by
JIMMIE V. MONACO

1. Once we were sweet - hearts,
2. You said you loved me,

Not so long a - go, Then I loved you so,
Not so long a - go, But you did - n't know,

# He Carved His Mother's Name Upon The Tree

Words by
HENRY V. NEAL

Music by
GUSSIE L. DAVIS

Slowly (*with expression*)

'Twas an or-phan boy one day, bear-ing wild flow'rs by the way, As
And he nev-er ceased to tell of the one he loved so well, But

to the cit-y grave-yard he was bound; Through the
cher-ished all her pre-cepts in his breast; So when

wick-et gate he sped, and he gent-ly bowed his head, And
Heav-en seemed to smile on his la-bors all the while, He

*Arr. by Hugo Frey*

laid them on a lit - tle grass - y mound; He was
plant - ed ros - es o'er her like the rest; Now the

poor, but at his side, where the rich and great had died, Were
or - phan, sad and lone, to a mer - chant prince has grown, A

mar - ble shafts and ros - es bloom - ing free; And 'mid
mon - u - ment of beau - ty you may see; It be -

flow'rs and sculp - tured stone, where she lay there long un - known, He
side the ma - ple stands, where in youth with lov - ing hands, He

carved his moth-er's name up-on the tree.

**Chorus, Slowly** (*with expression*)

Oh, the lit-tle or-phan boy, while the tear stood in his eye, Re-

mem-bered those sweet les-sons at her knee, And be-neath the ma-ple's shade, where in

si-lence she was laid, He carved his moth-er's name up-on the tree.

# You Never Miss The Water Till The Well Runs Dr

ROWLAND HOWARD

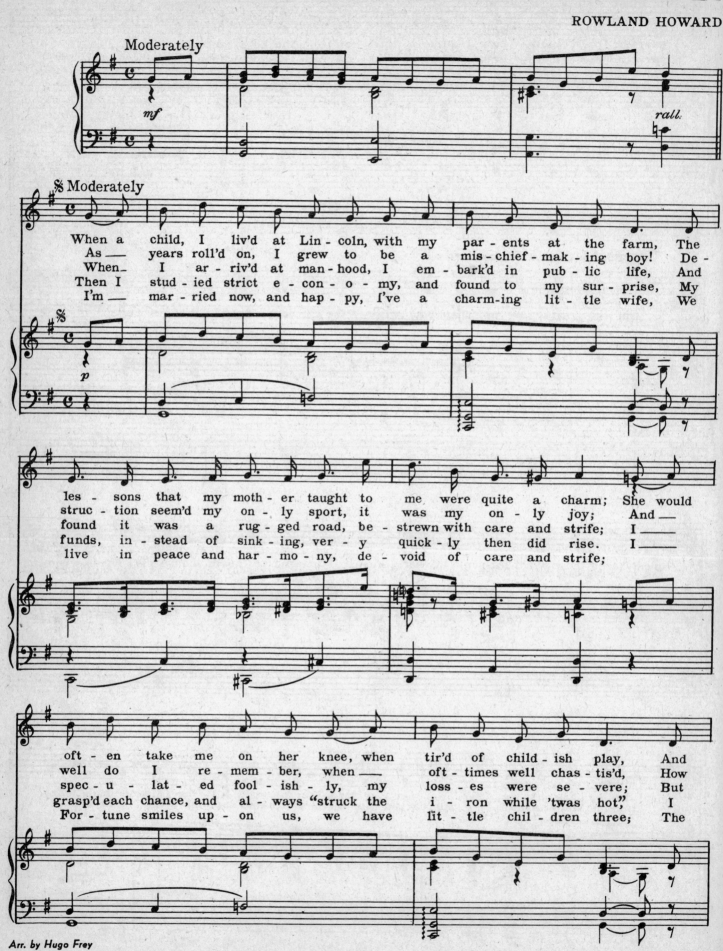

When a child, I liv'd at Lin-coln, with my par-ents at the farm, The
As years roll'd on, I grew to be a mis-chief-mak-ing boy! De-
When I ar-riv'd at man-hood, I em-bark'd in pub-lic life, And
Then I stud-ied strict e-con-o-my, and found to my sur-prise, My
I'm mar-ried now, and hap-py, I've a charm-ing lit-tle wife, We

les-sons that my moth-er taught to me were quite a charm; She would
struc-tion seem'd my on-ly sport, it was my on-ly joy; And
found it was a rug-ged road, be-strewn with care and strife; I
funds, in-stead of sink-ing, ver-y quick-ly then did rise. I
live in peace and har-mo-ny, de-void of care and strife;

oft-en take me on her knee, when tir'd of child-ish play, And
well do I re-mem-ber, when oft-times well chas-tis'd, How
spec-u-lat-ed fool-ish-ly, my loss-es were se-vere; But
grasp'd each chance, and al-ways "struck the i-ron while 'twas hot," I
For-tune smiles up-on us, we have lit-tle chil-dren three; The

*Arr. by Hugo Frey*

as she press'd me to her breast, I've heard my moth-er say:
fa - ther sat be - side me then, and thus has me ad - vis'd:
still a ti - ny lit - tle voice kept whis - p'ring in my ear,
seiz'd my op - por - tu - ni - ties, and nev - er once fer - got,
les - son that I teach them as they prat - tle 'round my knee,

**Chorus, Moderately**

Waste not, want not, is a max - im I would teach,

*mf*

Let your watch-word be 'des-patch' and 'prac-tice what you preach'; Do not let your chan - ces, like

sun-beams, pass you by, For "You nev - er miss the wa - ter till the well runs_ dry!"

D.S. %

Fine D.S.

# The Man Who Broke The Bank At Monte Carlo

FRED GILBERT

*Arr. by Hugo Frey*  Copyright 1942 **ROBBINS MUSIC CORPORATION**, 799 Seventh Ave., New York, N.Y.

Chorus, March tempo

As I walk a - long the Bois Boo - long. With an in - de - pen - dent air, ___ You can

hear the girls de - clare ___ "He must be a mil - lion - aire." ___ You can

hear them sigh and wish to die, You can see them wink the oth - er eye At the

man who broke the bank at Mon - te Car - lo. ___ As I lo. ___

# Paddle Your Own Canoe

H. CLIFTON

Arr. by HUGO FREY

Copyright 1939 by ROBBINS MUSIC CORPORATION, 799 Seventh Ave., New York, N. Y.

# Bonnie Eloise

C.W. ELLIOTT

J. R. THOMAS

# Rock Me To Sleep, Mother

Words by
**FLORENCE PERCY**

Music by
**ERNEST LESLIE**

Back-ward, turn back-ward, oh, time in your flight,
O - ver my heart, in the days that are flown,
Make me a child a - gain just for to - night!
No love like moth - er - love ev - er has shone,
Moth - er come back from the ech - o - less shore,
No oth - er wor - ship a - bides and en - dures,
Take me a - gain to your heart as of yore,
Faith - ful, un - self - ish, and pa - tient like yours;
Kiss from my fore - head the fur - rows of care,
None like a moth - er can charm a - way pain,
Smooth the few
From the sick

*Arr. by HUGO FREY*

Copyright 1939 by **ROBBINS MUSIC CORPORATION**, 799 Seventh Ave., New York, N. Y.
International Copyright Secured                    Made in U. S. A.

# At A Georgia Camp Meeting

KERRY MILLS

Arr. by Hugo Frey

# Where The Morning Glories Twine Around The Doo

Words by
ANDREW STERLING

Music by
HARRY VON TILZER

Arr. by Hugo Frey

Chorus, Slowly

Now, the same old moon is shin-ing, And the ros-es bloom as fair, And the

same dear hearts are pin-ing, They are wait-ing for me there. Moth-er

dear will come to meet me, And a sweet-heart's kiss will greet me, Where the

morn-ing glo-ries twine a-round the same old door.

# No! No! A Thousand Times No!!

AL SHERMAN
AL LEWIS
ABNER SILVER

Each time he threat-ened, "You'll wed me or else"
Win-ter would soon bring the snow and the cold,
She cried to him, "Though my fu-ture looks black, You
vil-lain sneered, "Black-smith, that maid-en is mine." The
life is con-ten-ted though sim-ple and plain, And

These were the words she'd ex-claim: _____
Yet she de-fied him and said: ____
buz-zard, my an-swer is still: ____
he-ro cried, "Not on your life!" ____
no more will she have to say: _____

**CHORUS**

1. No! No! a thous-and times No!
2. No! No! a thous-and times No!
3. No! No! a thous-and times No!
4. No! No! a thous-and times No!
5. No! No! a thous-and times No!

*)Small diagrams are optional

199

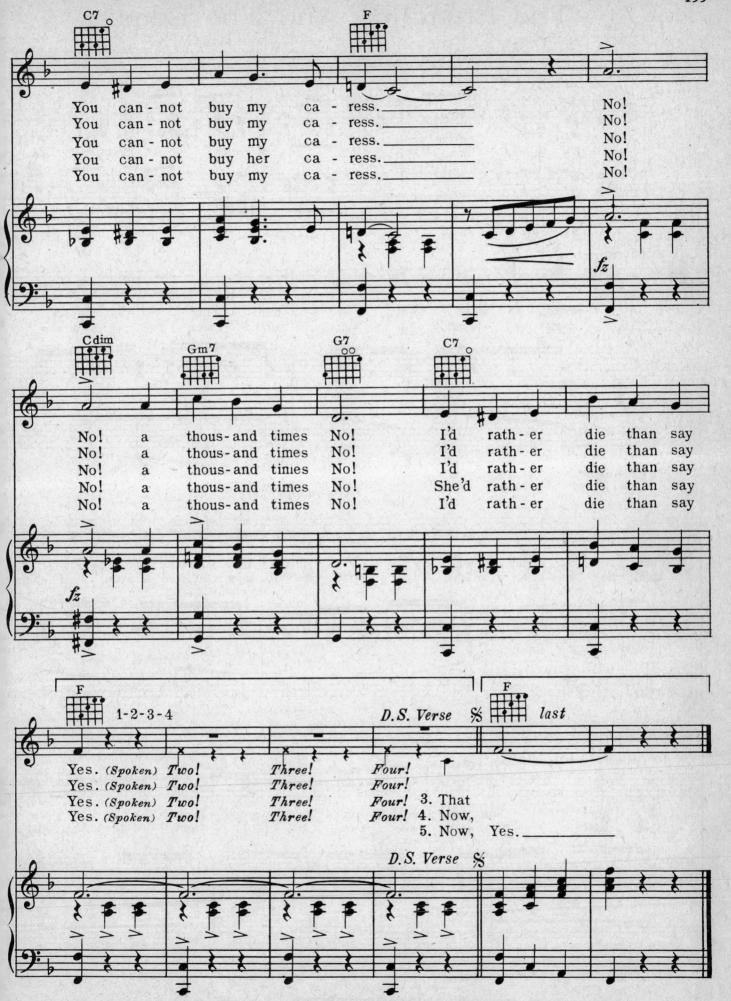

# The Preacher And The Bear

Words and Music by
JOE ARZONIA

*Arr. by Hugo Frey*

shot him-self some ver-y fine quail and one big meas-ly
a-bout then the limb let go and the man came tumb-ling

hare, And on his way re-turn-ing home he met a
down, You should have seen him get his raz-or out be-

great big grizz-ly bear The bear marched out in the
fore he struck the bear ground He hit the ground cut-ting

mid-dle of the road and he waltzed to the man you see, The
right and left, 'tis true he put up a ver-y game fight; Just

man got so ex - cit - ed that he climbed a per - sim - mon
then the bear hugged this man he squeezed him a lit - tle too

tree The bear sat down up - on the ground and the
tight, The man he then lost his raz - or but the

man climbed out on a limb, He cast his eyes to the
bear held on with a vim, He cast his eyes to the

God in the skies and these words he said— to him.
God in the skies and once more he said— to him.

**Chorus, Moderately**

"Oh Lord, didn't you de-liv-er Dan-iel from the Li-on's den? Al-

so ___ de-liv-er Jo-nah from the bel-ly of the whale and then, Three

He-brew chil-dren from the fie-ry fur-nace, so the good books do ___ de-clare. Now

Lord ___ if you can't help me for good-ness sake don't you help that bear." bear."

# Good Morning, Carrie!

Words by
R. C. MᶜPHERSON

Music by
SMITH and BOWMAN

*Arr. by Hugo Frey*

# Where Is My Wandering Boy Tonight?

REV. ROBERT LOWRY

Arr. by Hugo Frey

joy and light, The child of my love and prayer? _____
heart and more true, And none was so sweet as he. _____
home a joy, And life was a mer-ry chime. _____
all his blight, And tell him I love him still! _____

**Chorus, Slow** *(with expression)*

O, where is my boy to - night? _____ O,

where is my boy to - night? _____ My heart o'er - flows, for I

love him, he knows; O, where is my boy to - night? _____

# Daisies Won't Tell

Words and Music by
ANITA OWEN

Moderate Waltz time

There's a sweet old sto - ry You have heard be - fore,____
In a dream I fan - cied You were by my side.____

Here a - mong the dai - sies Let me tell it o'er;____
While I gath - ered dai - sies One long chain you tied,____

On - ly say you love me, For I love you well,____
'Round us both I wound it, Close I held you, too,____

An - swer with a kiss, dear, Dai - sies nev - er tell.____
Dai - sies nev - er tell, dear, Make that dream come true.____

*Arr. by Hugo Frey*

# Sweet Marie

C. WARMAN

RAYMOND MOORE

Arr. by Hugo Frey

# Peggy Mine

Words and Music by
MAURICE STONEHILL

**Andante.**

It's a long road we have travelled and the end is might-y nigh, Peg-gy
We have seen a heap o' chang-es on our jour-ney, me and you, Peg-gy

mine, _____ Peg-gy mine! _____ Hand in hand we've gone to-geth-er, scarce a
mine, _____ Peg-gy mine! _____ On the hill side o-ver yon-der, sleep a

tear has dimmed our eye, Peg-gy mine, _____ Peg-gy mine! _____ It
host of folks we knew; Peg-gy mine, _____ Peg-gy mine! _____ But

LEO FEIST, INC., 1629 Broadway, New York, N. Y.

**CHORUS**.

Balm - y Spring-tide's left us, so has Sum - mer's glow,

Gol - den Au - tumn's past us with the days of long a - go,

Now we've come to Win-ter, sil - ver'd locks are thine, still we're sweethearts, you an' I, dear

Peg - gy mine, we'll be sweet-hearts till we die, dear Peg - gy mine.

# Love's Old Sweet Song
## Just A Song At Twilight

Words by
**C. CLIFTON BINGHAM**

Music by
**J. L. MOLLOY**

**Very Slow** (*with Feeling*)

Just a song at twi-light, when the lights are low, And the flick-'ring shad-ows soft-ly come and go; Tho' the heart be wea-ry, Sad the day and long, Still to us at twi-light comes love's old song, Comes Love's Old Sweet Song.

**Slow** (*with expression*)

E-ven to-day we hear love's song of yore, Deep in our heart it dwells for ev-er more. Foot-steps may fal-ter, wea-ry grow the way

# Just Because She Made Dem Goo-Goo Eyes

JOHN QUEEN and
HUGHIE CANNON

Cake walk tempo

Arr. by Hugo Frey

got to stand a fine" he lost his job, ——— for quite a while. ———
blow the road right here, if you'll be mine, ——— if you'll be mine. ———
eat with-out no dough, so here I am, ——— out in— the snow."

**Chorus, Moderato**

*mp-mf*

Just be-cause she made them Goo-Goo eyes ——— I

thought I'd won— a home and copp'd a prize ——— She

is the best what is ——— and I need her in my biz, Just be-cause she

makes them Goo-Goo eyes. ———

1.

2.

eyes. ———

*fz*

# Say "Au Revoir," But Not "Goodbye"

HARRY KENNEDY

1. Say "Au Re- voir" But Not "Good-bye," For part-ing brings a bit-ter sigh; The past is gone, though mem'ry gives, One cling-ing thought the fu-ture lives; Our du-ty first, love must not lead, What might have been, had fate de-creed; 'Twere bet-ter far had we not met, I loved you then, I love you yet.

2. The wa-ters glide, the oars lie still, A rip-pling laugh, a word at will; 'Where an gels fear, fools dare to tread', Shall live for years, tho' past is dead; This one good-bye must be our last, The word is spoke, the die is cast; But still my heart throbs wild with pain, And tho' we ne'er shall meet a-gain.

Robbins Music Corporation, New York, N. Y.

Say "Au Re - voir" But Not "Good-bye", Though past is dead, love can-not die, 'Twere bet-ter

far had we not met, I loved you then, I love you yet.

## Wait For The Wagon

R. B. BUCKLEY

Brightly

1. Will you come with me, my Phil - lis dear, To yon blue moun-tain free? Where
2. Where the riv - er runs like sil - ver, And birds they sing so sweet, I

blos-soms smell the sweet-est, Come, rove a - long with me. Wait For The Wag-on,
have a cab - in, Phil - lis, And some-thing good to eat. Wait For The Wag-on,

Wait For The Wag-on, Wait For The Wag - on and we'll all take a ride.

# Oh, My Darling Clementine

By
P. MONTRO

Copyright 1942 **ROBBINS MUSIC CORPORATION**, 799 Seventh Ave., New York, N. Y.
International Copyright Secured
Made in U. S. A.

# My Old Dutch

CHAS. INGLE

ain't a la-dy liv-in' in the land, As I'd swop for my dear Old Dutch.

# The Old Gray Mare

Lively

Oh, The Old Gray Mare, She ain't what she used to be, Ain't what she used to be,

Ain't what she used to be. The Old Gray Mare, She ain't what she used to be,

Man - y long years a - go. _____ Man - y long years a -

Fine

go _____ Man - y long years a - go. _____ Oh, The

D.S. al Fine

# Go To Sleep, Lena Darling
## (Emmet's Lullaby)

J. K. Emmet

Andante

Close your eyes, Le-na, my dar-ling, While I sing your lull-a-by; Fear thou no dan-ger, Le-na,
Bright be de morn-ing, my dar-ling, Ven you ope your eyes; Sun-beams glow all round you, Le-na,

Move not, dear Le-na, my dar-ling, For your broth-er watch-es nigh you, Le-na dear.
Peace be with thee, love, my dar-ling, Blue and cloud-less be the sky for Le-na dear.

An-gels guide thee, Le-na dear, my dar-ling, Noth-ing e-vil can come near;
Birds sing their bright songs for thee, my dar-ling, Full of sweet-est mel-o-dy;

Bright-est flow-ers blow for thee, Dar-ling sis-ter, dear to me.
An-gels ev-er hov-er near, Dar-ling sis-ter, dear to me.

Go to sleep, go to sleep, my ba - by, my ba - by, my ba - by;

Go to sleep, my ba - by; ba - by, oh, bye, Go to sleep, Le - na, sleep.

## Rock-A-Bye, Baby

Slowly with expression

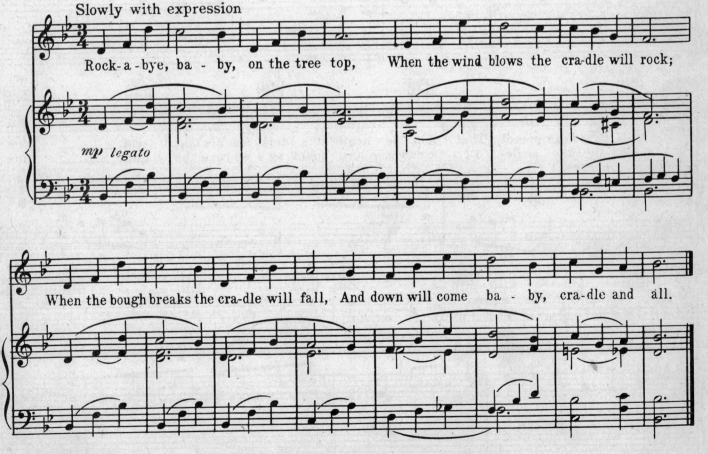

Rock-a-bye, ba - by, on the tree top, When the wind blows the cra-dle will rock;

mp legato

When the bough breaks the cra-dle will fall, And down will come ba - by, cra-dle and all.

Arr. by HUGO FREY

Copyright 1939 Robbins Music Corporation, New York, N. Y.
International Copyright Secured

# The Little Old Red Shawl My Mother Wore

CHARLES MORELAND

Robbins Music Corporation, New York, N. Y.

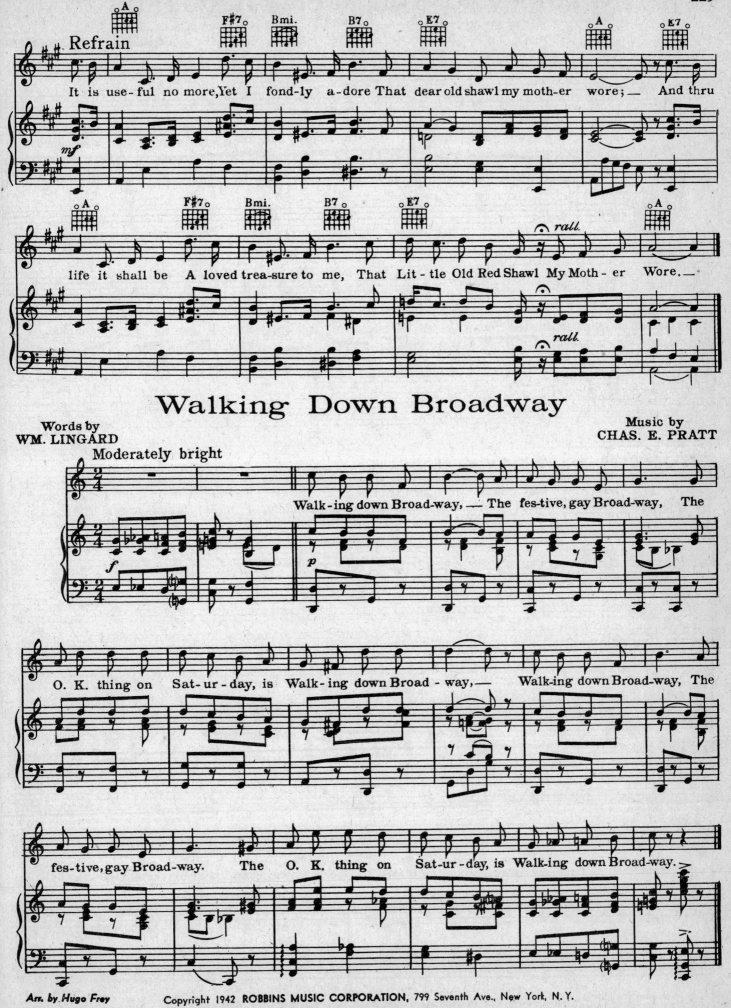

# Walking Down Broadway

Words by
**WM. LINGARD**

Music by
**CHAS. E. PRATT**

Arr. by Hugo Frey

# Where Did You Get That Hat?

JOSEPH J. SULLIVAN

**Moderately**

Now, how I came to get this hat, 'Tis ver-y strange and fun-ny; My
If I go to the Op-'ra House in the op-'ra seas-on; There's

grand-fa-ther died and left to me his prop-er-ty and mon-ey; And when the will it was read out, they
some-one sure to shout at me, with-out the slight-est reas-on, If I go to a chow-der club, to

told me straight and flat; If I would have his mon-ey, I must al-ways wear his hat!
have a jol-ly spree; There's some-one in the par-ty, who is sure to shout at me:

**Chorus, Moderately**

Where did you get that hat? Where did you get that tile? Isn't it a nob-by one, and just the proper style;

I should like to have one, just the same as that! Where-e'er I go they shout, "Hel-lo, where did you get that hat?"

# Over The Hill To The Poor House

GEO. L. CATLIN

DAVID BRAHAM

# Just Tell Them That You Saw Me

PAUL DRESSER

Moderate (ballad style)

While stroll - ing down the street one eve up - on mere pleas - ure bent, 'Twas
"Your cheeks are pale, your face is thin, come tell me were you ill, When

af - ter busi-ness wor - ries of the day ___ I saw a girl who shrank from me in
last we met your eyes shone clear and bright ___ Come home with me when I go Madge, the

whom I rec - og - nized, My school-mate in a vil - lage far a - way. ___ "Is
change will do you good, Your moth - er won-ders where you are to - night" ___ "I

that you Madge," I said to her, she quick - ly turned a - way, "Don't
long to see them all a - gain, but not just yet" she said, "'Tis

Copyright 1942 ROBBINS MUSIC CORPORATION, 799 Seventh Ave., New York, N.Y.

# She Was Happy 'Till She Met You

CHARLES GRAHAM

MONROE ROSENFELD

*Arr. by Hugo Frey*

ev-'ry spark of love for him has fled;—— There he sought her out at last, With re-
law for-bids you part us, we are wed!—— "But you've brok-en ev-'ry vow, She is

pen-tance for the past, But her moth-er met him at the door and said:——
yours no long-er now, My— daugh-ter shall not go!" the moth-er said.——

Chorus

She Was Hap-py 'Till She Met You, And the fault is all your own, If she

wish-es to for-get you, You will please leave her a-lone. She has come to her old moth-er, Just be-

cause there is no oth-er, She'll be hap-py in her own sweet home.——

# The Sunshine Of Paradise Alley

WALTER H. FORD

JOHN W. BRATTON

Arr. by Hugo Frey

# In The Evening By The Moonlight

JAMES A. BLAND

Slowly

Arr. by Hugo Frey

# I Don't Want To Play In Your Yard

Words by
PHILIP WINGATE

Music by
H. W. PETRIE

Once there lived, side by side, two lit-tle maids; Used to dress just a-like,
Next day, two lit-tle maids each oth-er miss; Quar-rel is soon made up;

hair down in braids. Blue ging-ham pin-a-fores, stock-ings of red,
sealed with a kiss. Then, hand in hand a-gain, hap-py they go,

Lit-tle sun bon-nets tied on each pret-ty head. When school was o-ver,
Friends all through life to be, they love each oth-er so. Soon school days pass a-way

*Arr. by Hugo Frey*

*rall.*     *a tempo*

se-crets they'd tell,    Whis-per-ing arm in arm    down by the   well;—   One day   a
sor-rows and bliss,    But love re - mem-bers, yet,    quar-rel and   kiss; In sweet dreams of

quar-rel came,    hot tears were shed,    "You can't play in our yard!" but the oth-er said:
child - hood   we hear the   cry:    "You can't play in our yard!" and the old re - ply:

**Lightly**

I Don't Want To Play In Your Yard,   I don't like you an-y more.    You'll be sor-ry when you

C    G7    C7    F    C7

see me Slid - ing down our cel-lar door.    You can't hol - ler down our rain barrel,

You can't climb our ap-ple tree.—   I Don't Want To Play In Your Yard, If you won't be good to me.

# I'll Take You Home Again, Kathleen

Words and Music by
THOMAS P. WESTENDORF

1. I'll Take You Home A-gain, Kath-leen,____ A-cross the o-cean wild and wide,__ To
2. I know you love me, Kath-leen, dear,____ Your heart was ev-er fond and true;__ I
3. To that dear home be-yond the sea,____ My Kath-leen shall a-gain re-turn,__ And

where your heart has ev-er been,____ Since first you were my bon-nie bride.__ The
al-ways feel when you are near,____ That life holds noth-ing dear, but you.__ The
when thy old friends wel-come thee,____ Thy lov-ing heart will cease to yearn.__ Where

ro-ses all have left your cheek,____ I've watched them fade a-way and die;__ Your
smiles that once you gave to me,____ I scarce-ly ev-er see them now,__ Tho'
laughs the lit-tle sil-ver stream,____ Be-side your moth-er's hum-ble cot,__ And

voice is sad when-e'er you speak,____ And tears be-dim your lov-ing eyes.__
man-y man-y times I see,____ A dark-'ning shad-ow on your brow.__
bright-est rays of sun-shine gleam,____ There all your grief will be for-got.__

**Transcription by HUGO FREY**

# Home, Sweet Home

JOHN HOWARD PAYNE
SIR HENRY BISHOP

# Comrades

FELIX McGLENNON

With a swing

Com - rades, Com - rades, ev - er since we were boys, ___

Shar - ing each oth - er's sor - rows, Shar - ing each oth - er's joys; ___

Com - rades when man-hood was dawn - ing, Faith - ful what e'er may be - tide; ___

When dan - ger threat-en'd, my jol - ly old com - rade was there by my side. ___

# Little Brown Jug

Lively

My wife and I live all a - lone, in a lit - tle brown hut we call our own. She loves gin, and I love rum, Tell you what it is, Don't we have fun?

**Refrain**

Ha! Ha! Ha! 'tis you and me, Lit-tle Brown Jug, Don't I love thee Ha! Ha! Ha! 'tis you and me, Lit-tle Brown Jug Don't I love thee.

## Wait Till The Clouds Roll By

H. T. FULMER

**With spirit**

Wait Till The Clouds Roll By; Jen-ny, Wait Till The Clouds Roll By,

Jen-ny, my own true loved one, Wait Till The Clouds Roll By. ____

## My Nelly's Blue Eyes

Wᵐ J. SCANLAN

**Gracefully**

My Nel-ly's Blue Eyes, ____ My Nel-ly's Blue Eyes,

Bright-er than stars, that shine at night, My Nel-ly's Blue Eyes. ____

Robbins Music Corporation, New York, N. Y.

# You And I

CLARIBEL

Smoothly

We sat by the riv-er, You And I,— In the sweet sum-mer time, long a - go,— So

smooth-ly the wa-ter glid-ed by,— Mak-ing mu-sic in its tran-quil flow;— We threw two leaf-lets, You And

I,— To the riv-er as it wan-der'd on,— And one was rent and left to die,— And the

oth-er float-ed for-ward all a - lone,— And Oh! we were sad-den'd, You And I,— For we

felt that our youth's gold-en dream, Might fade, and our lives be sev-er'd soon,— As the two leaves were part-ed on the stream.

Robbins Music Corporation, New York, N. Y.

# Sing Again That Sweet Refrain

GUSSIE L. DAVIS

# Jeanie With The Light Brown Hair

Words and Music by
Stephen C. Foster

# Shoo, Fly, Don't Bother Me!

**Words by
Billy Reeves**

Music by
Frank Campbell

# Always Take Mother's Advice!

JENNIE LINDSAY

Al-ways take moth-er's ad-vice,____ She knows what is best for your
Hon-or your moth-er, so dear,____ You'll ne'er know her worth 'till she's

good;____ Let her kind words then suf-fice,____ And
gone;____ Re-spect her grey hair while she's here,____ You'll be

nev-er speak has-ty or rude;____ Re-mem-ber that she is the
sad when she leaves you a-lone.____ On earth you will ne'er have an-

Arr. by Hugo Frey

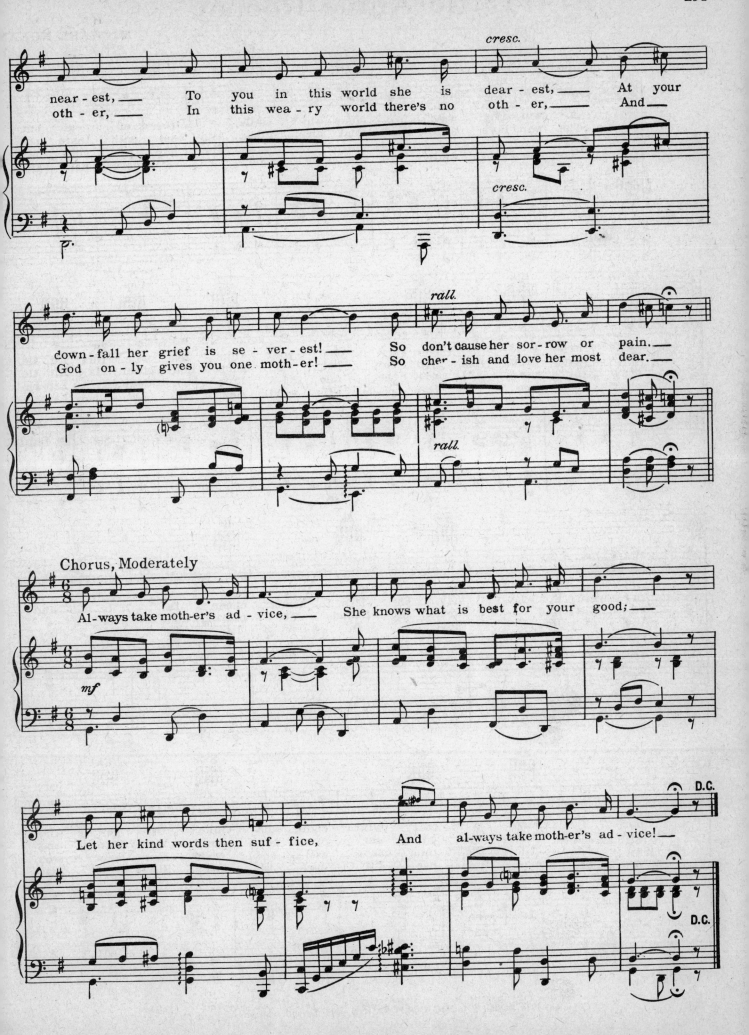

near - est, ___ To you in this world she is dear - est, ___ At your
oth - er, ___ In this wea - ry world there's no oth - er, ___ And ___

down - fall her grief is se - ver - est! ___ So don't cause her sor - row or pain, ___
God on - ly gives you one moth - er! ___ So cher - ish and love her most dear. ___

Chorus, Moderately

Al - ways take moth-er's ad - vice, ___ She knows what is best for your good; ___

Let her kind words then suf - fice, And al-ways take moth-er's ad - vice! ___

D.C.

# Little Annie Rooney

MICHAEL NOLAN

Arr. by Hugo Frey

# You Tell Me Your Dream, I'll Tell You Mine

Lyric by
SEYMOUR RICE and
ALBERT H. BROWN

Music by
CHARLES N. DANIELS

Piano Arr. by
Hugo Frey